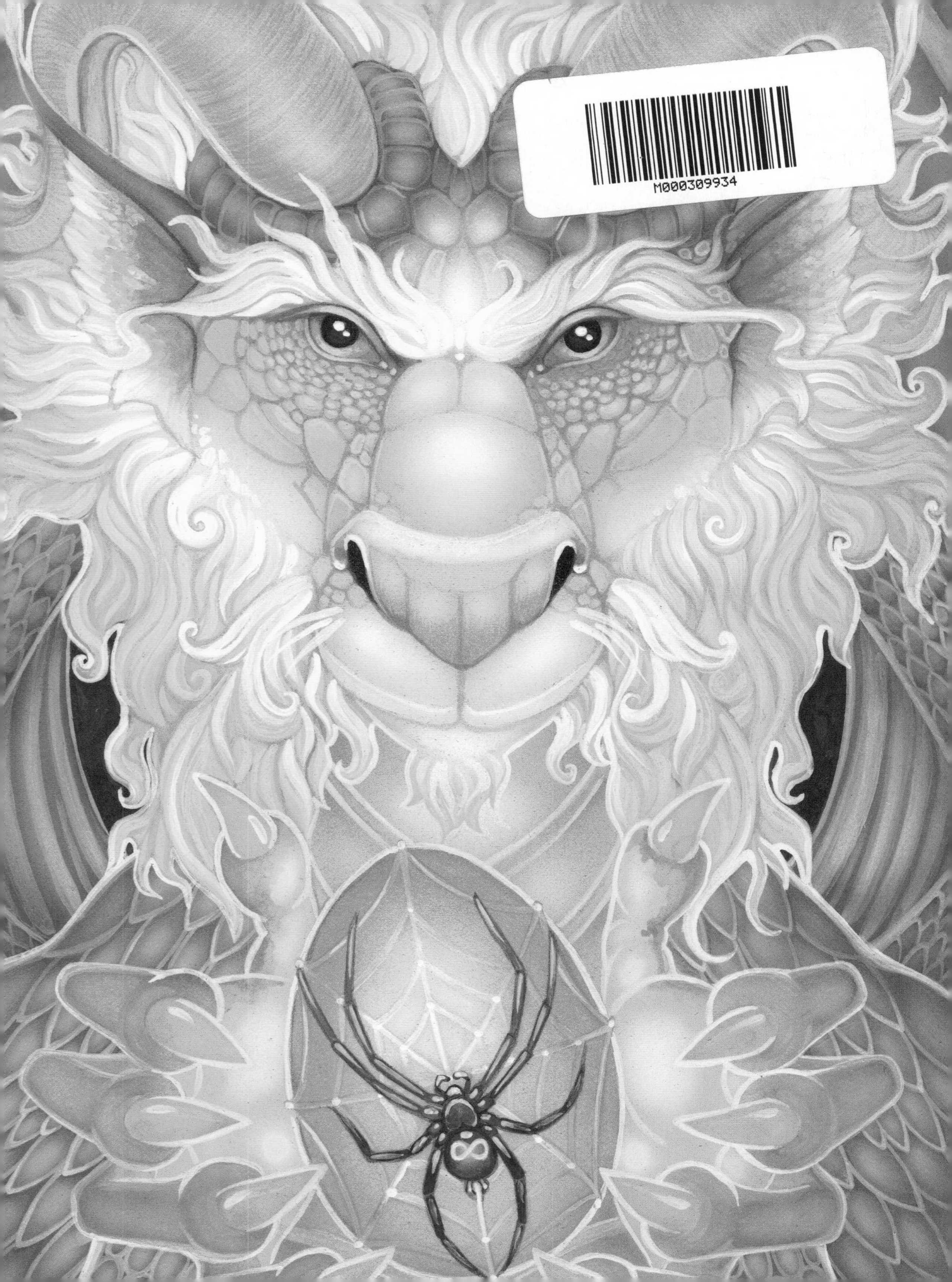

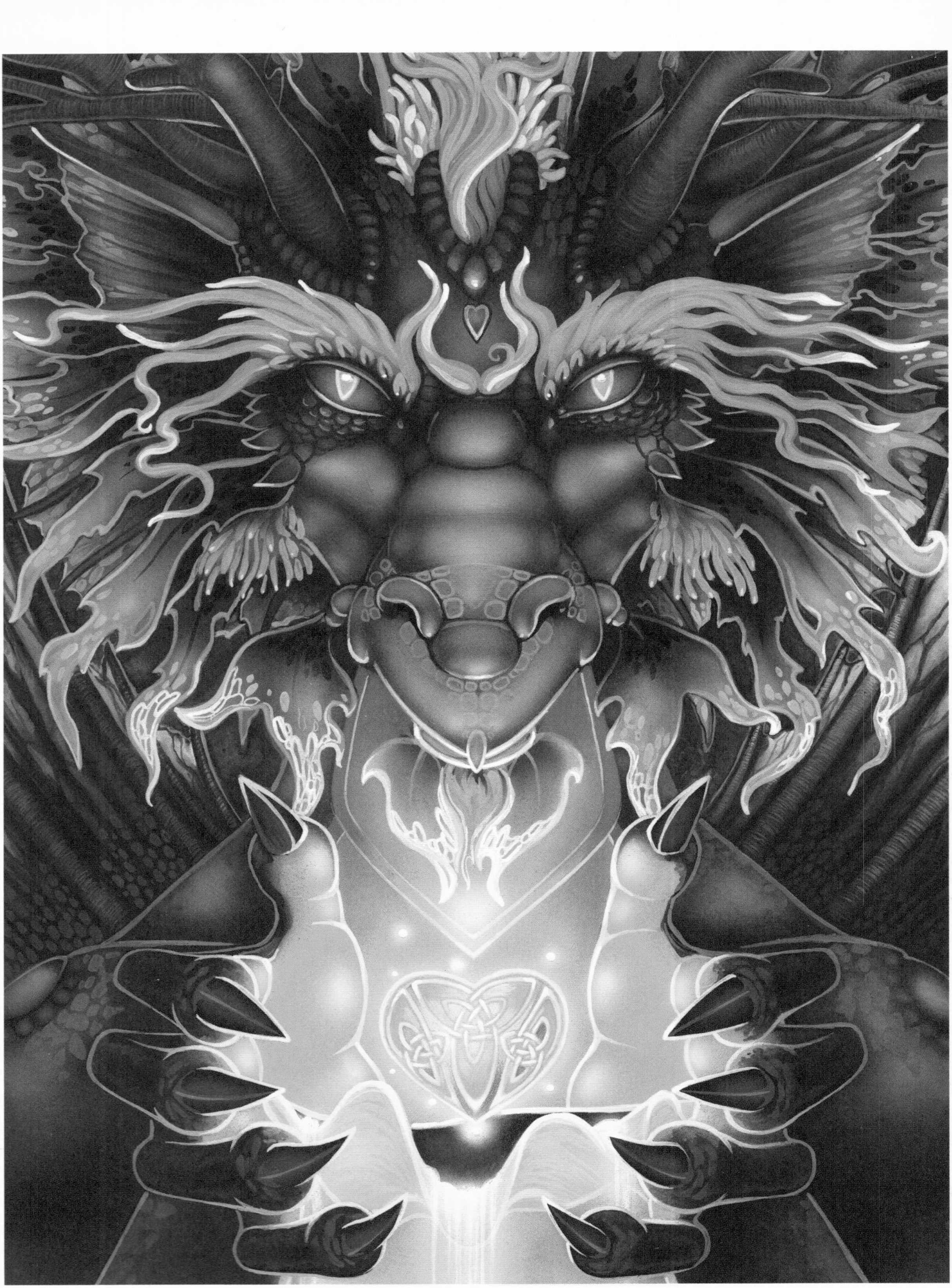

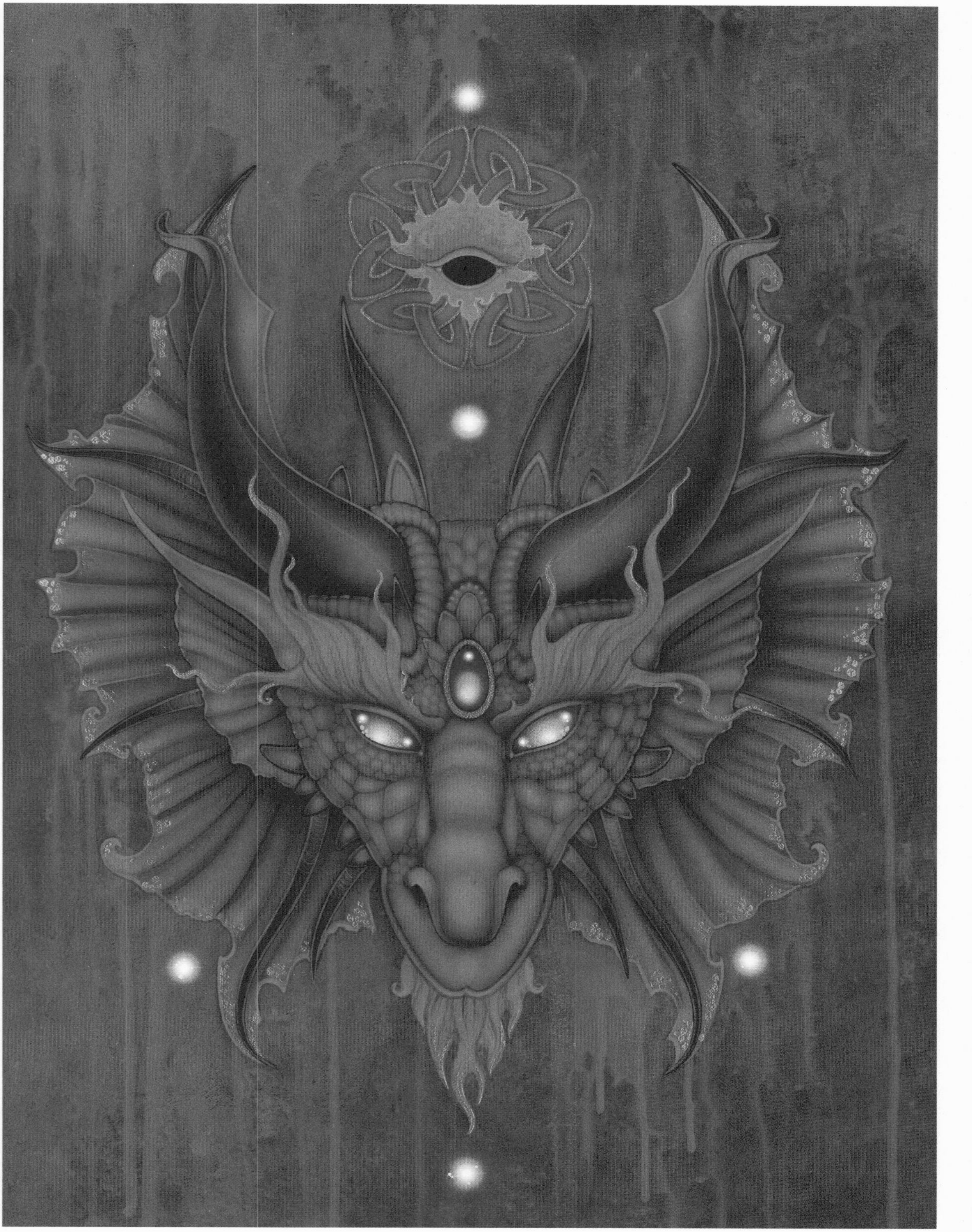

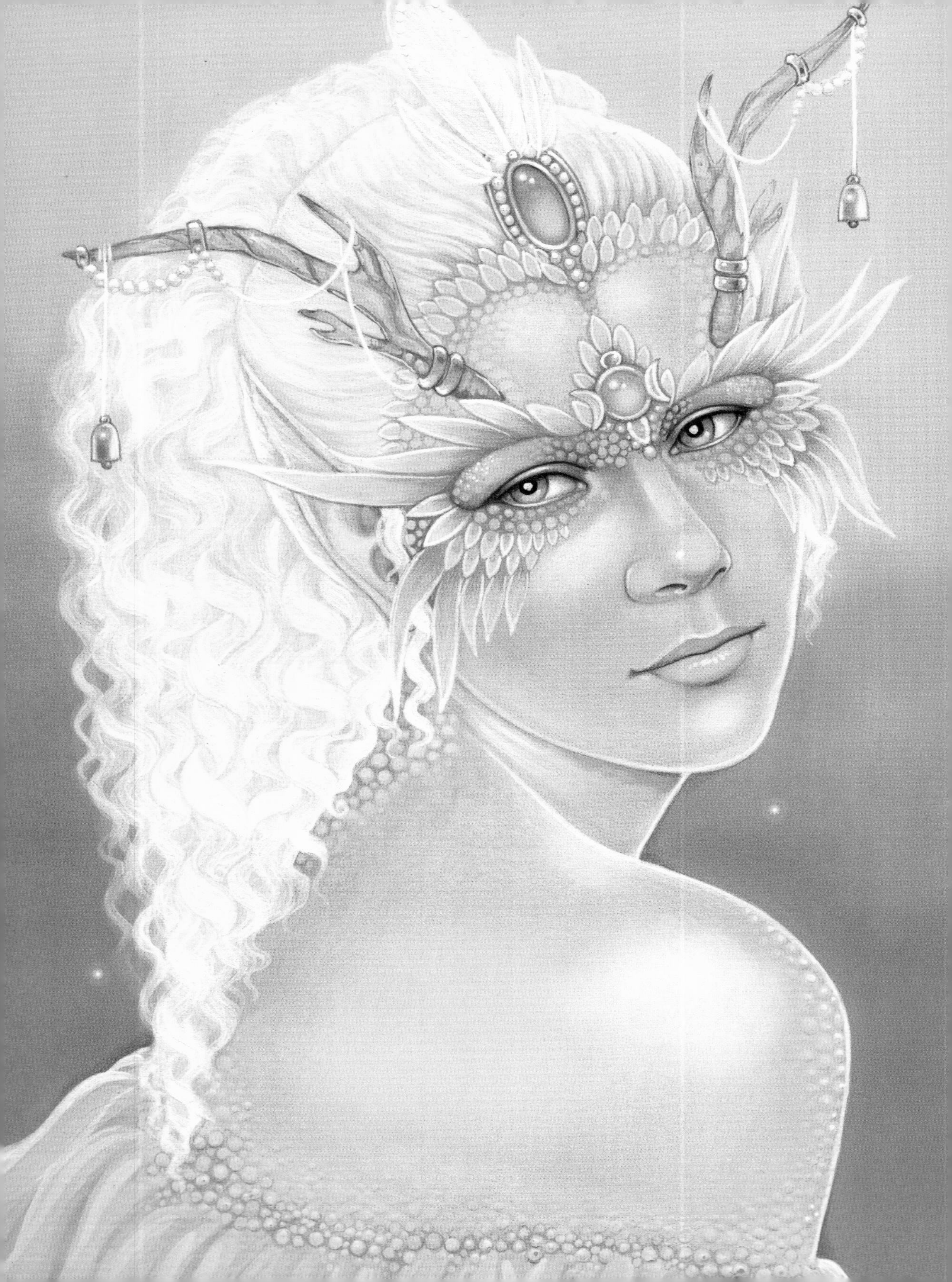

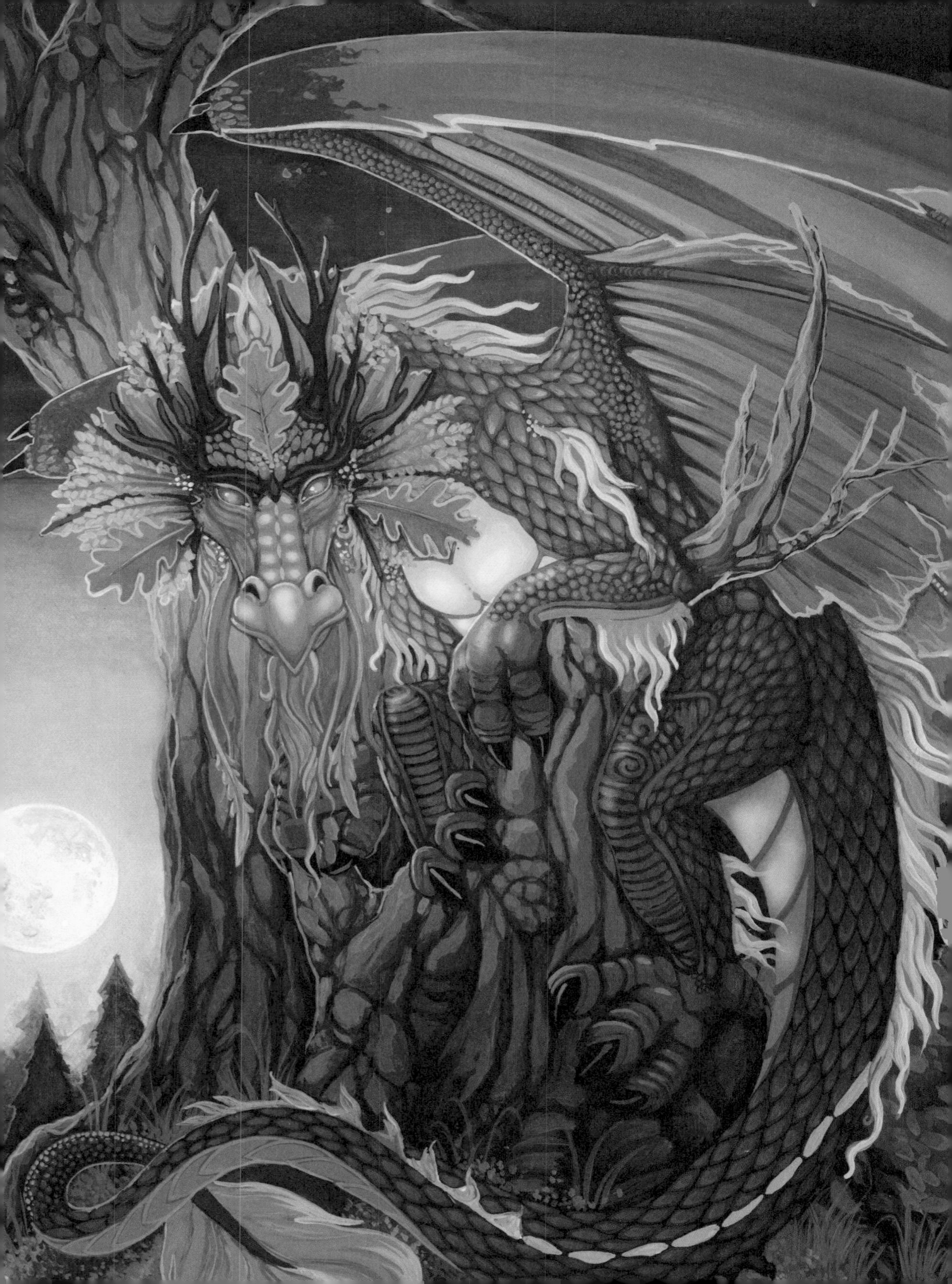

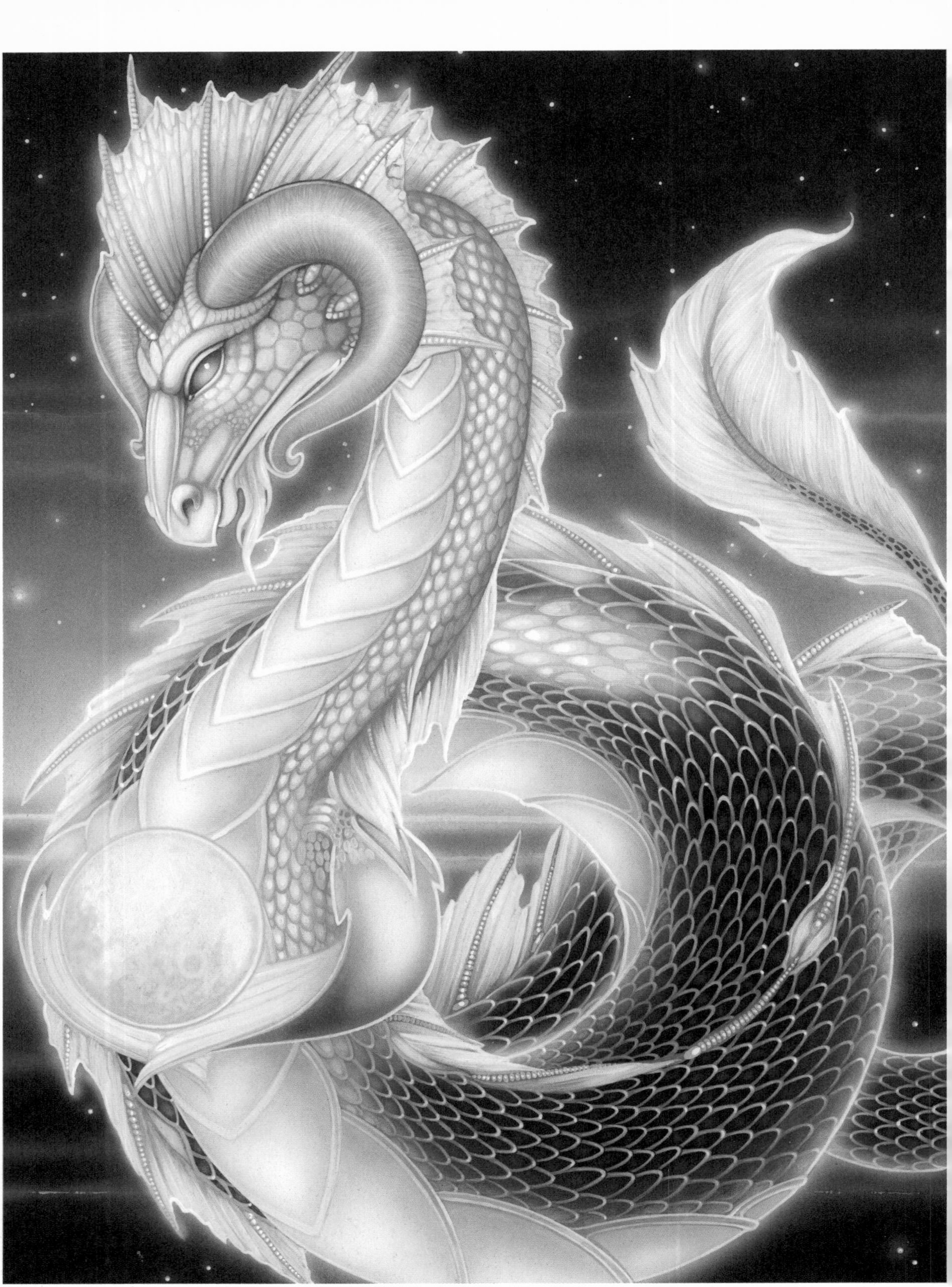

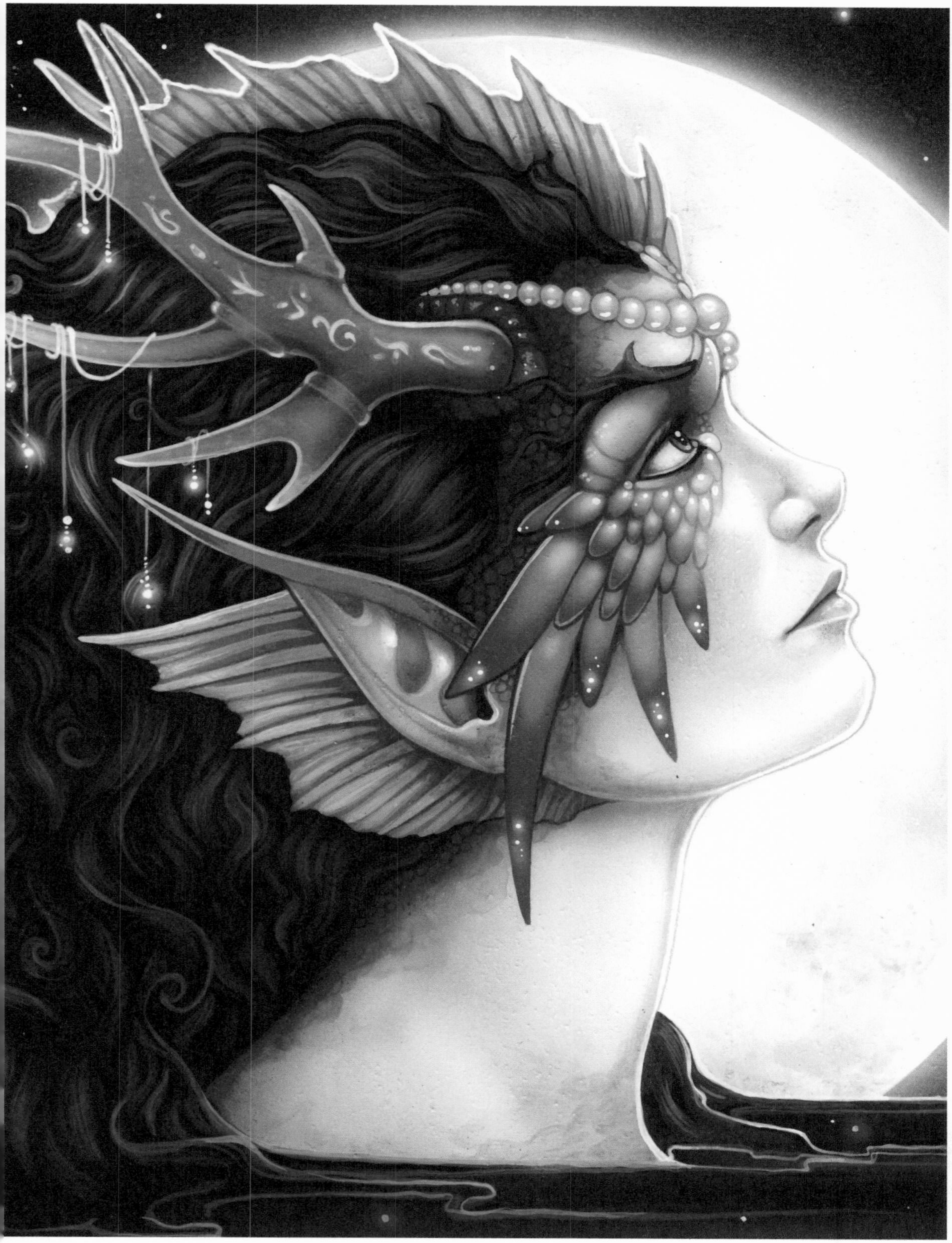

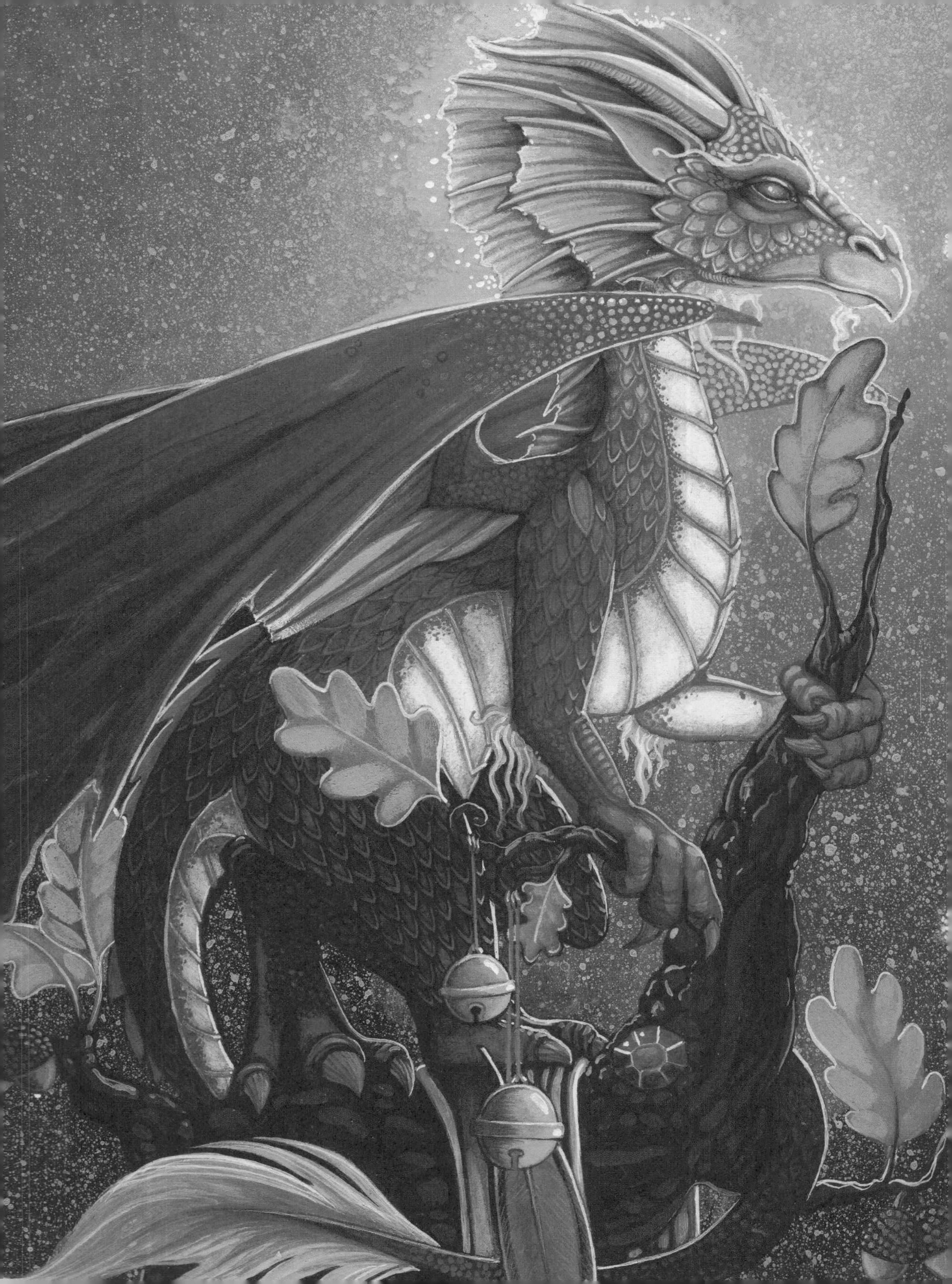

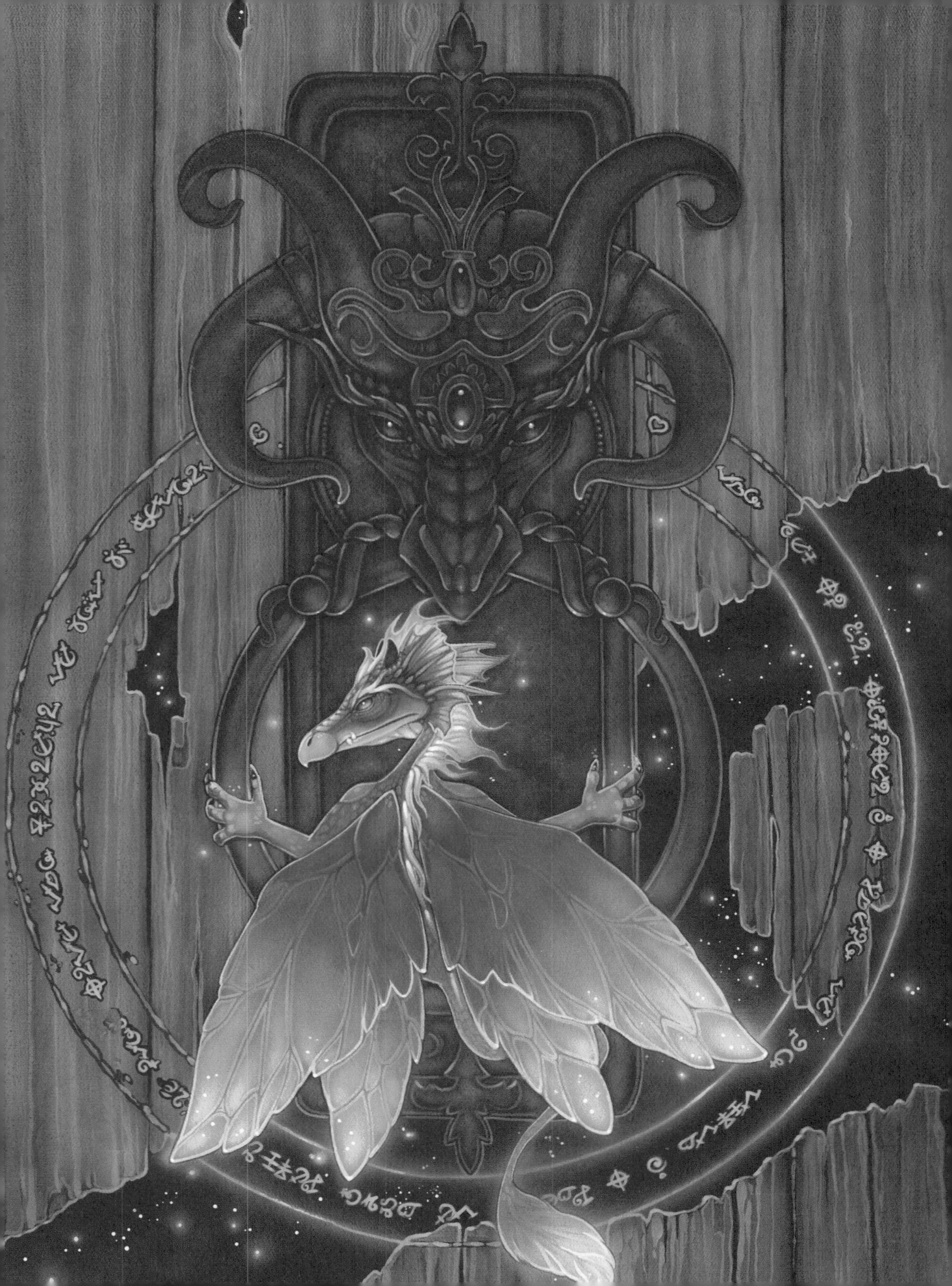

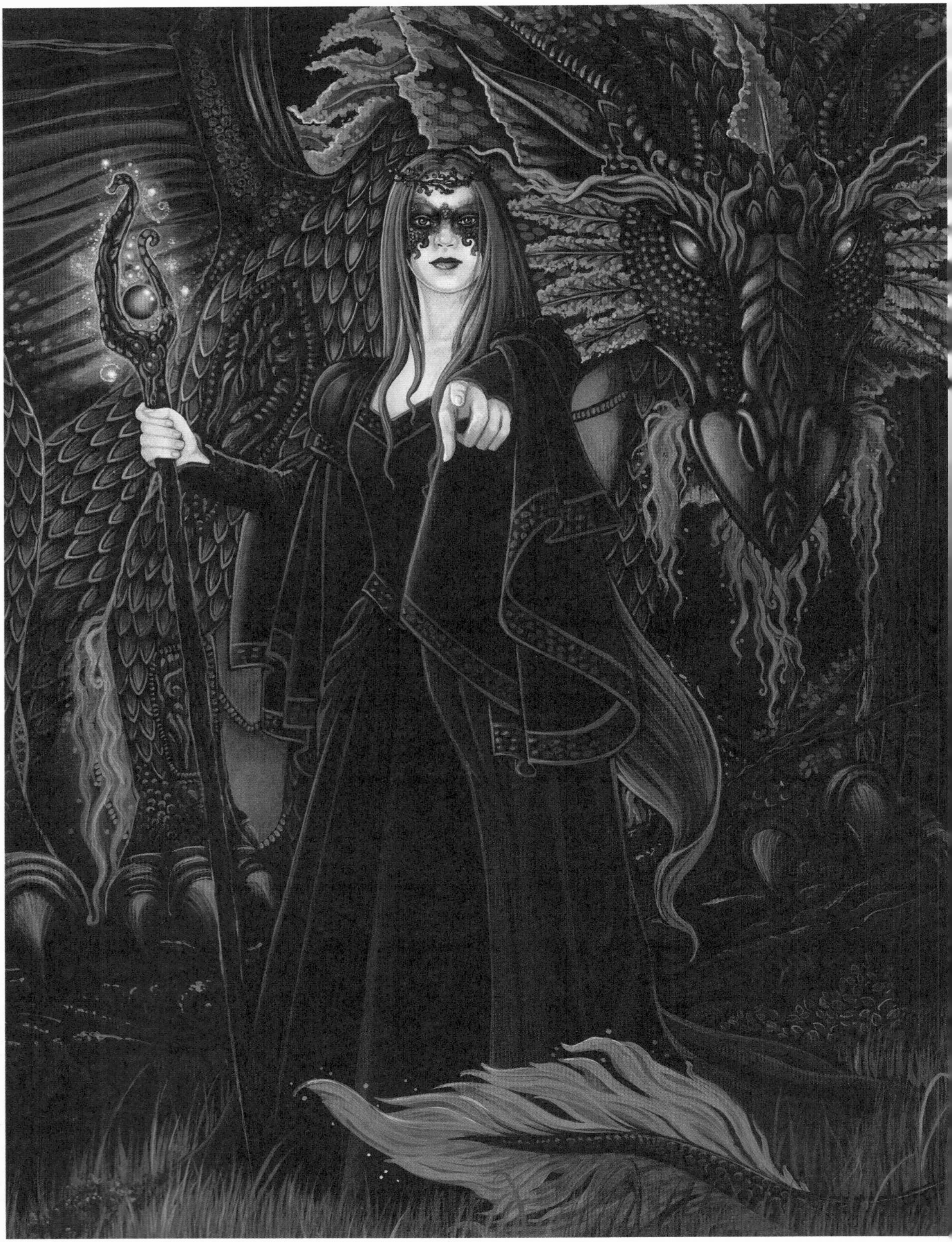

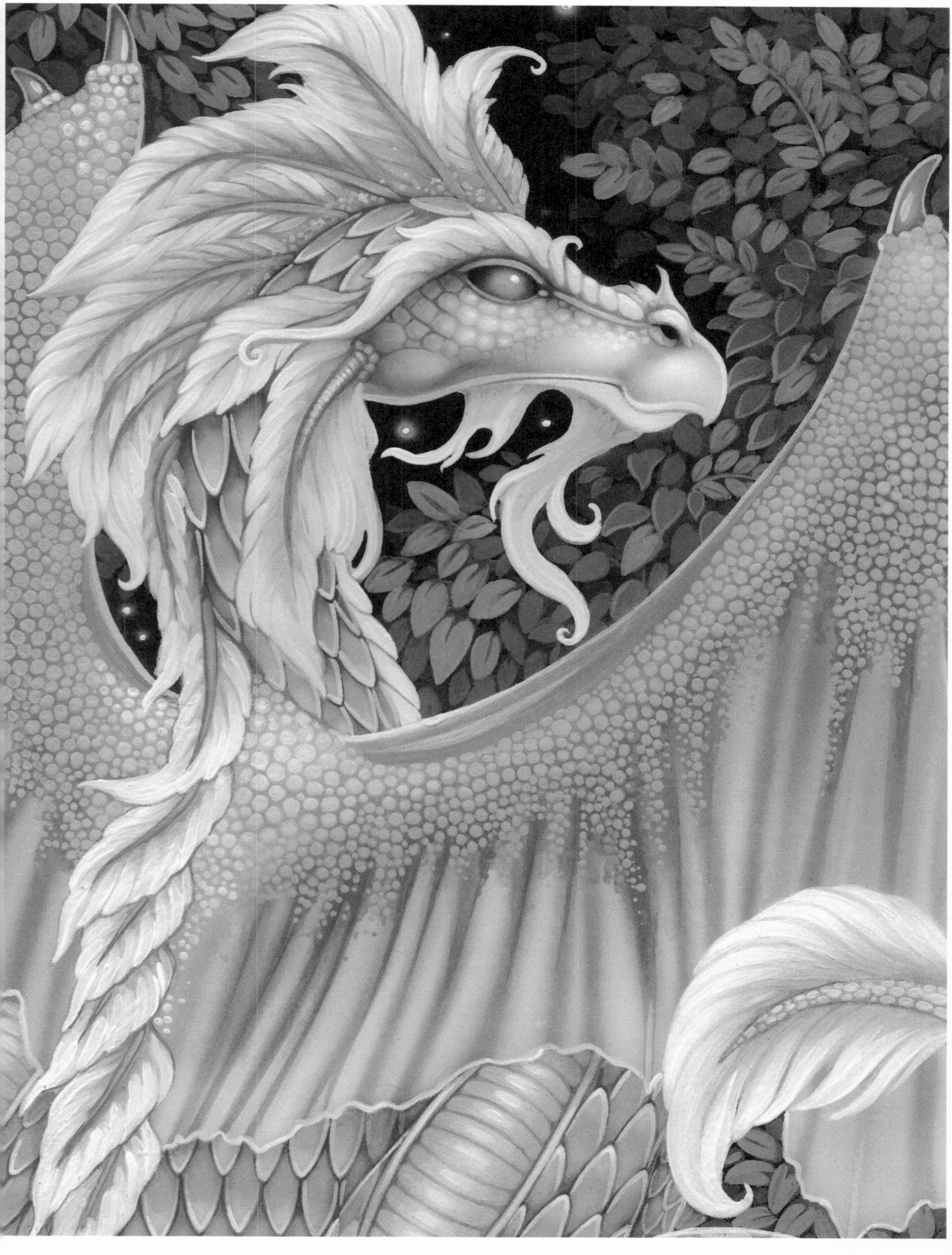

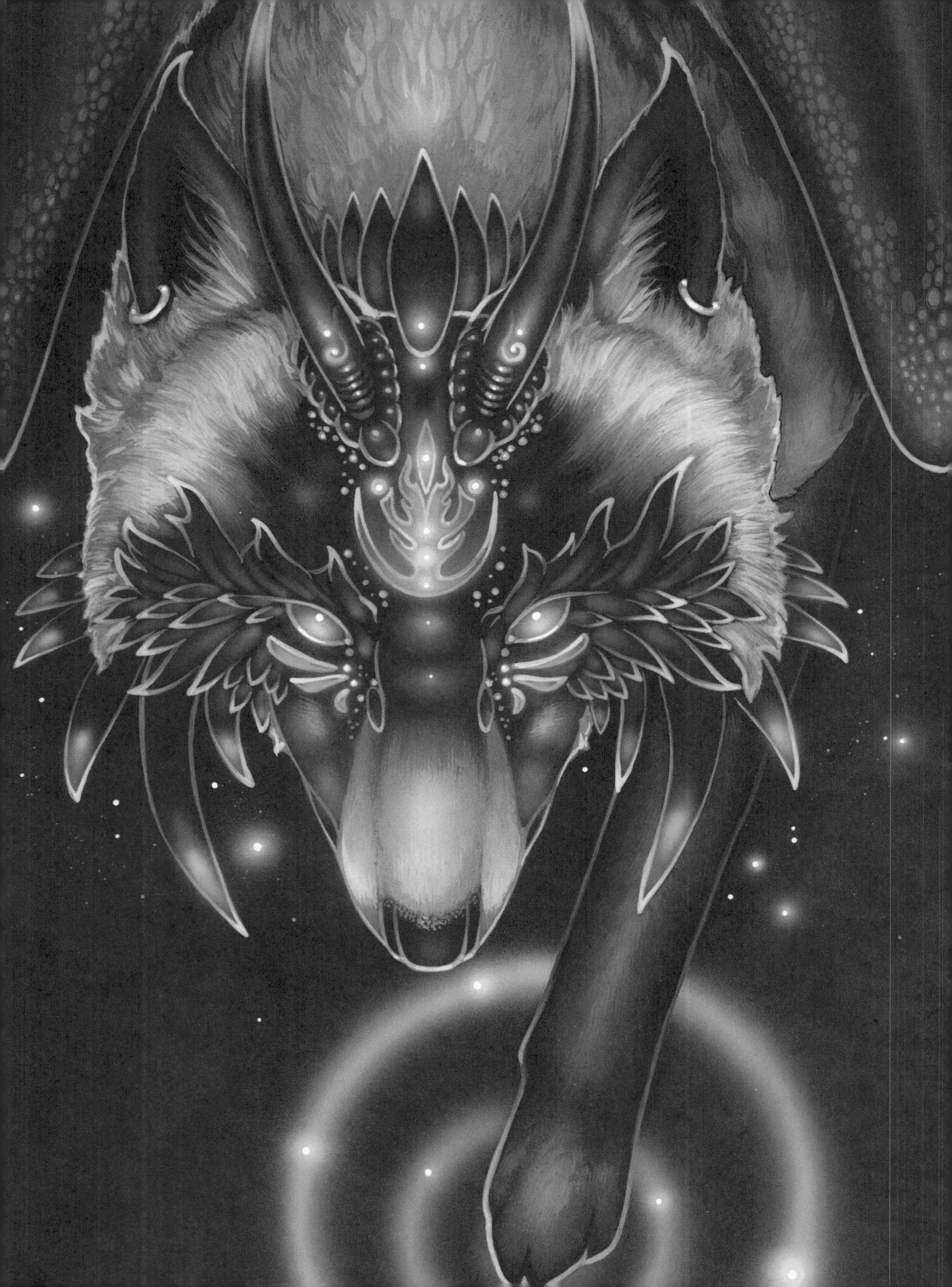

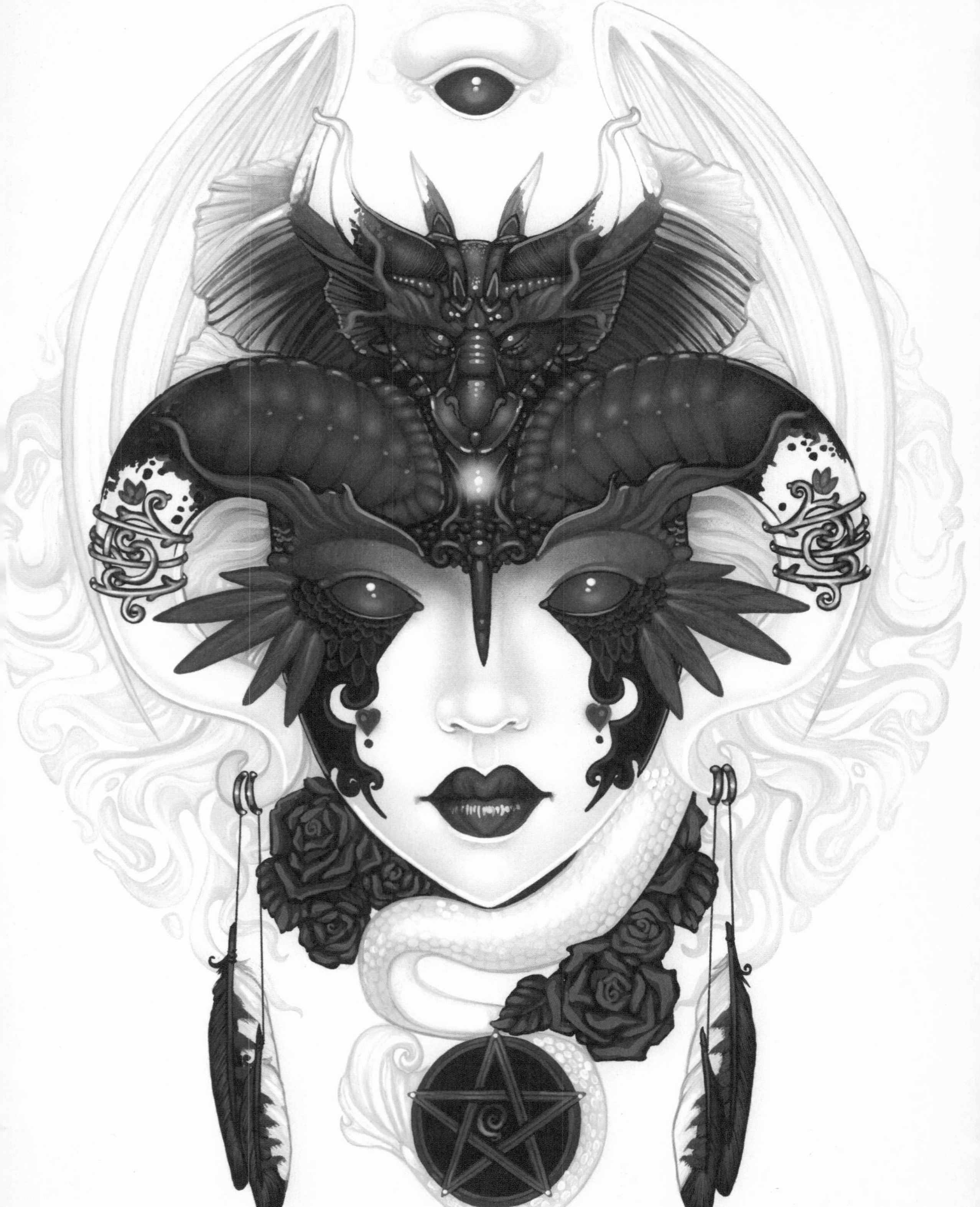

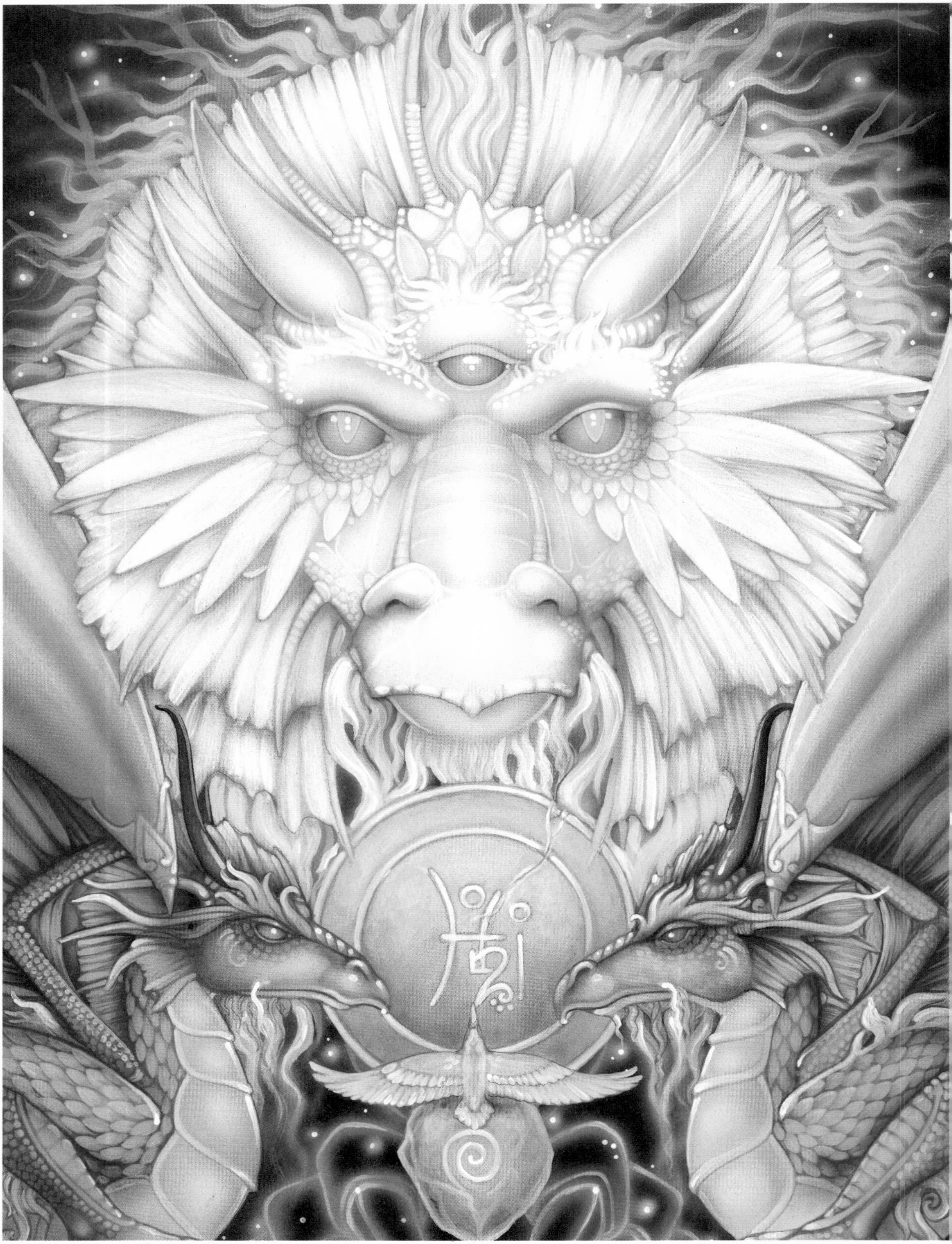

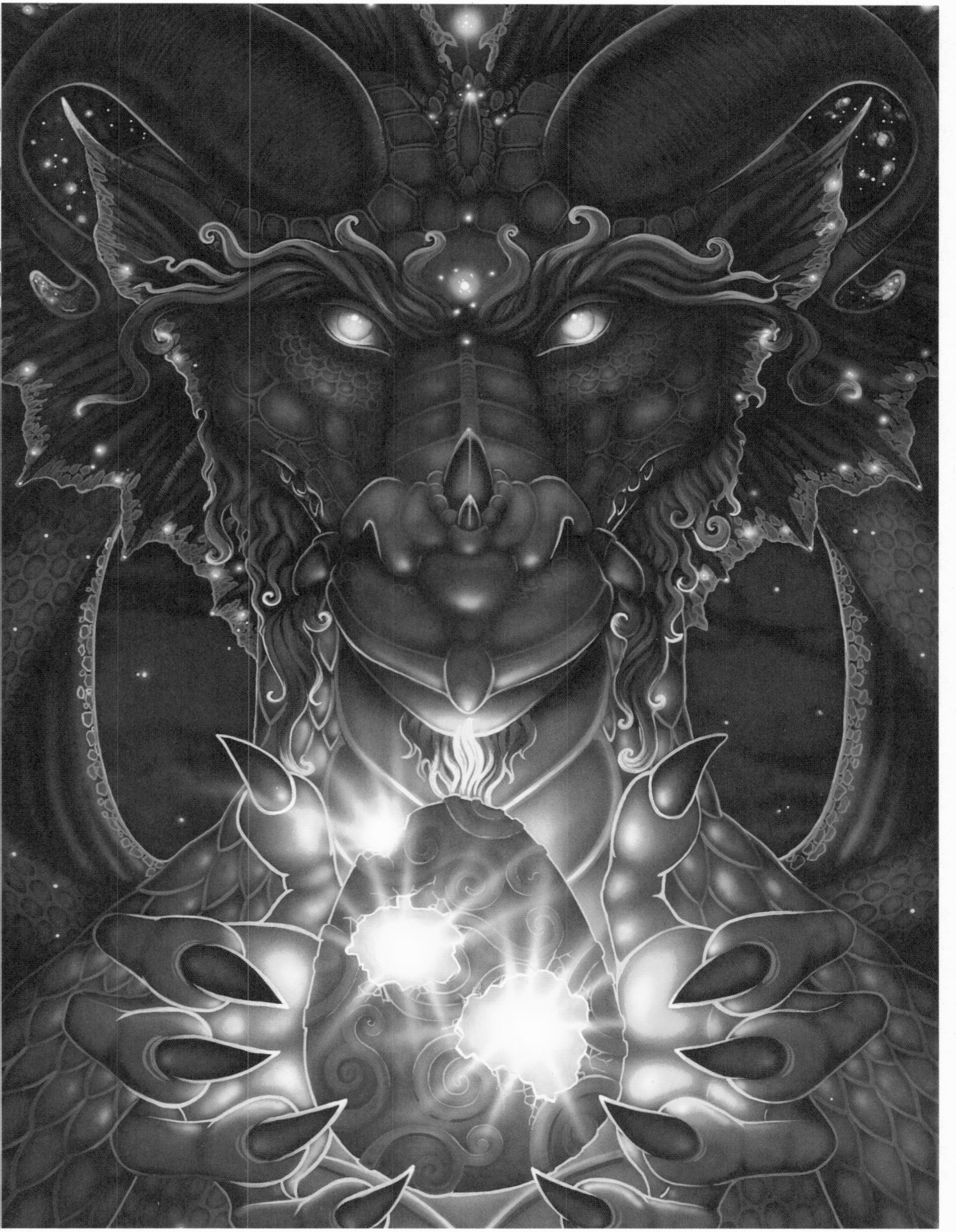

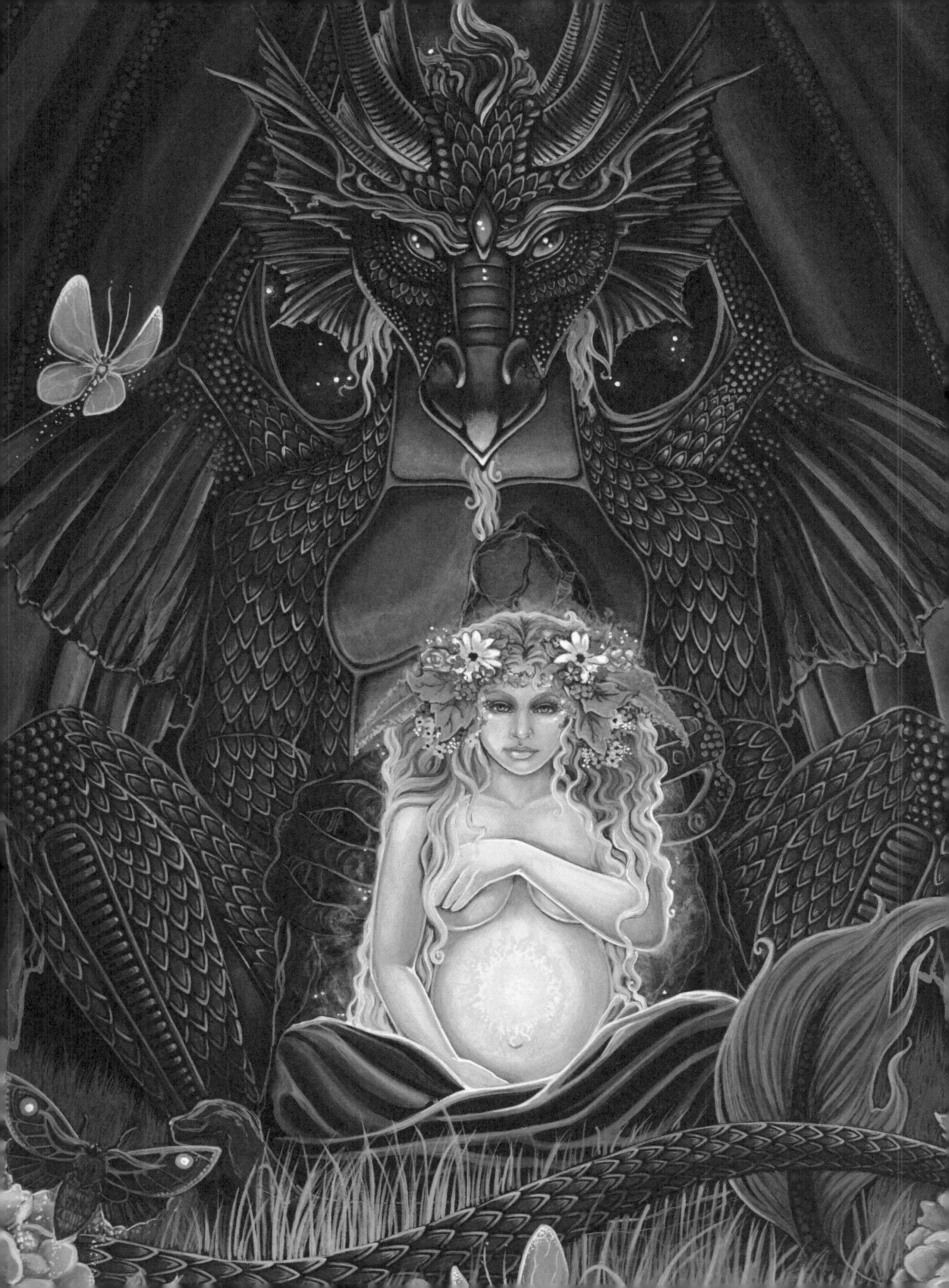

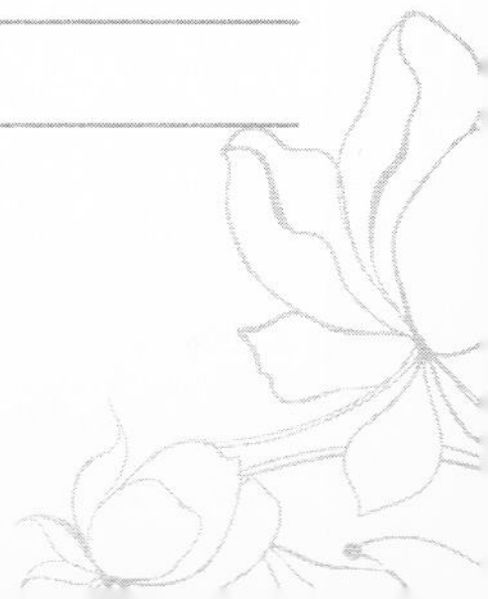

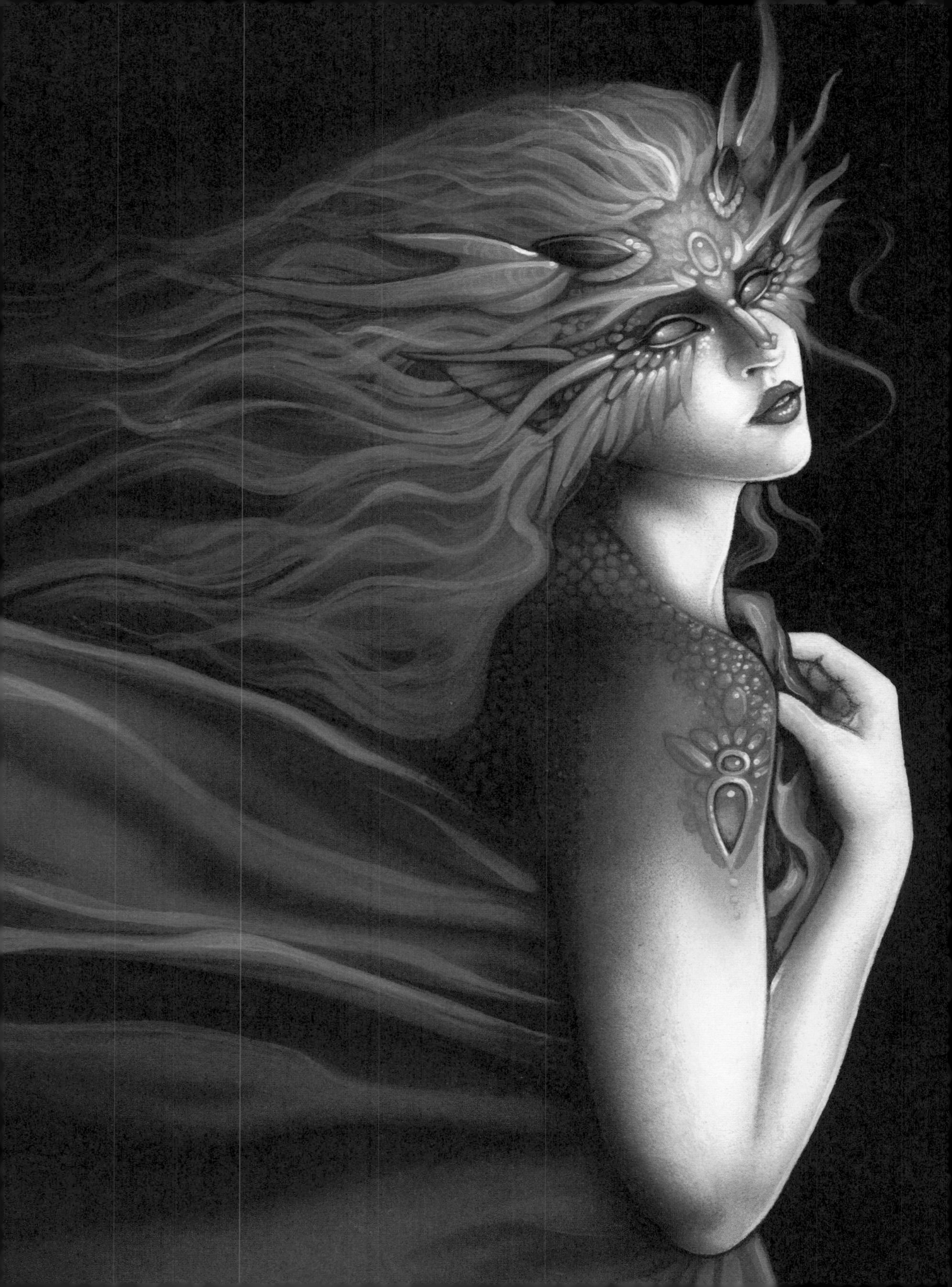

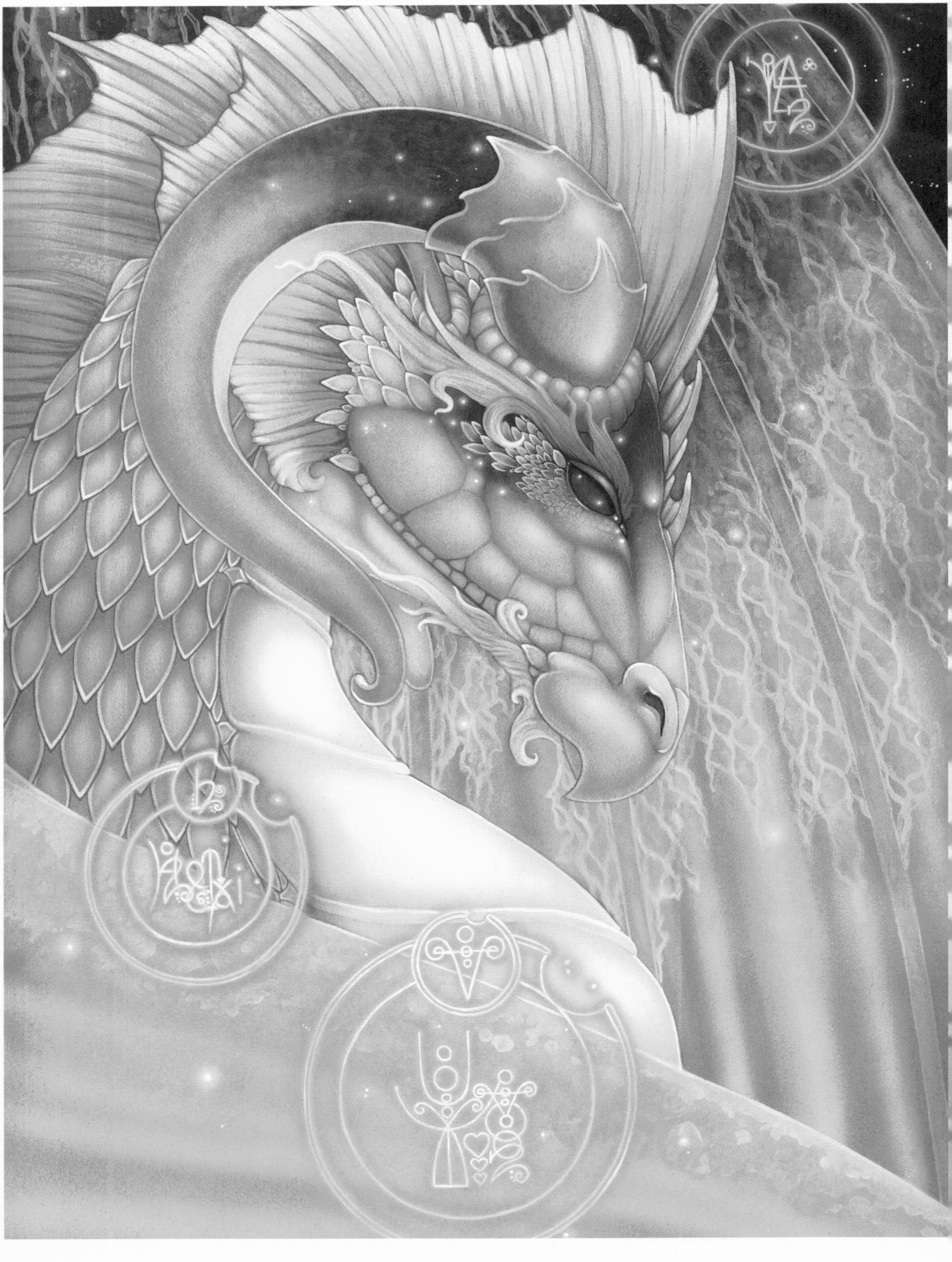

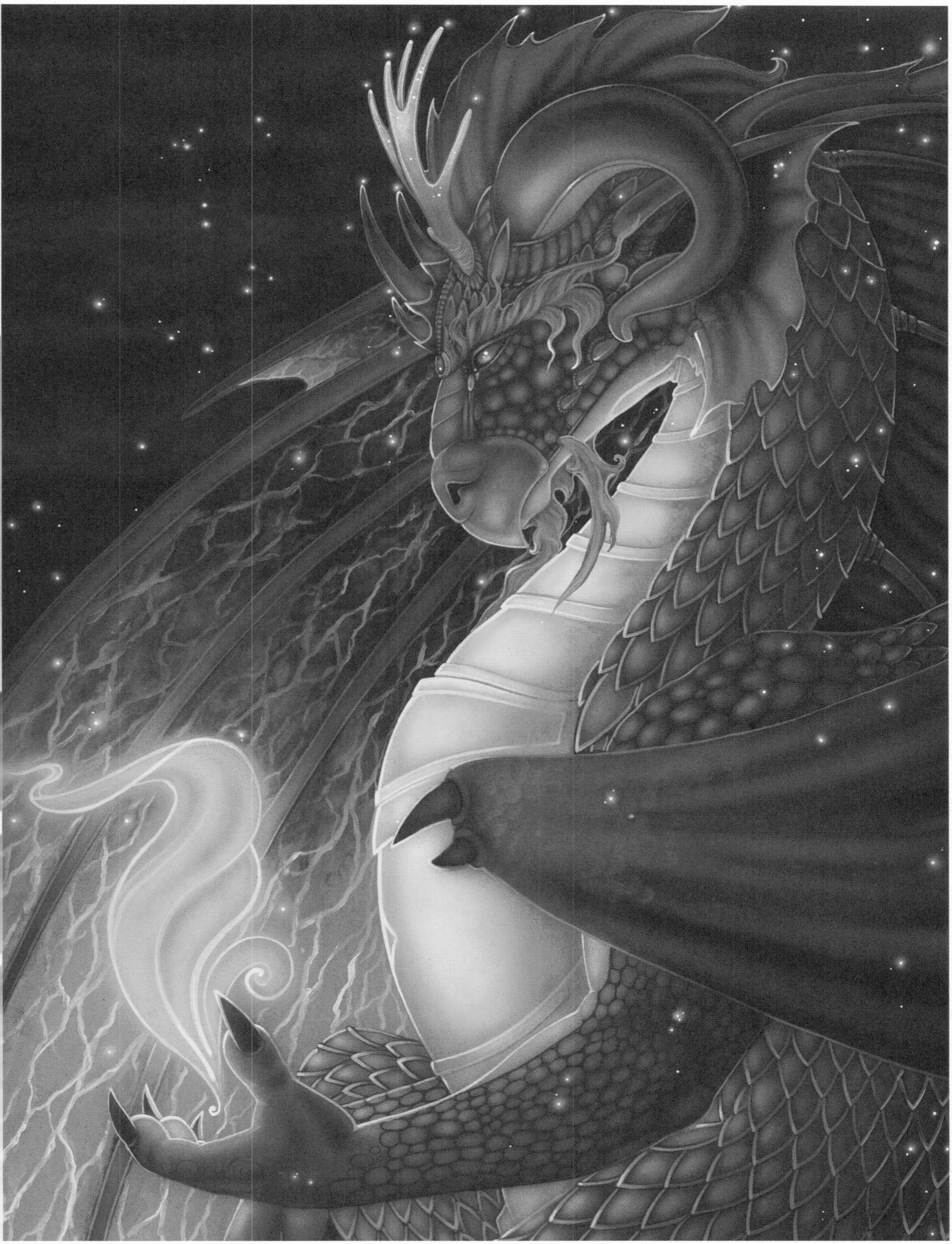

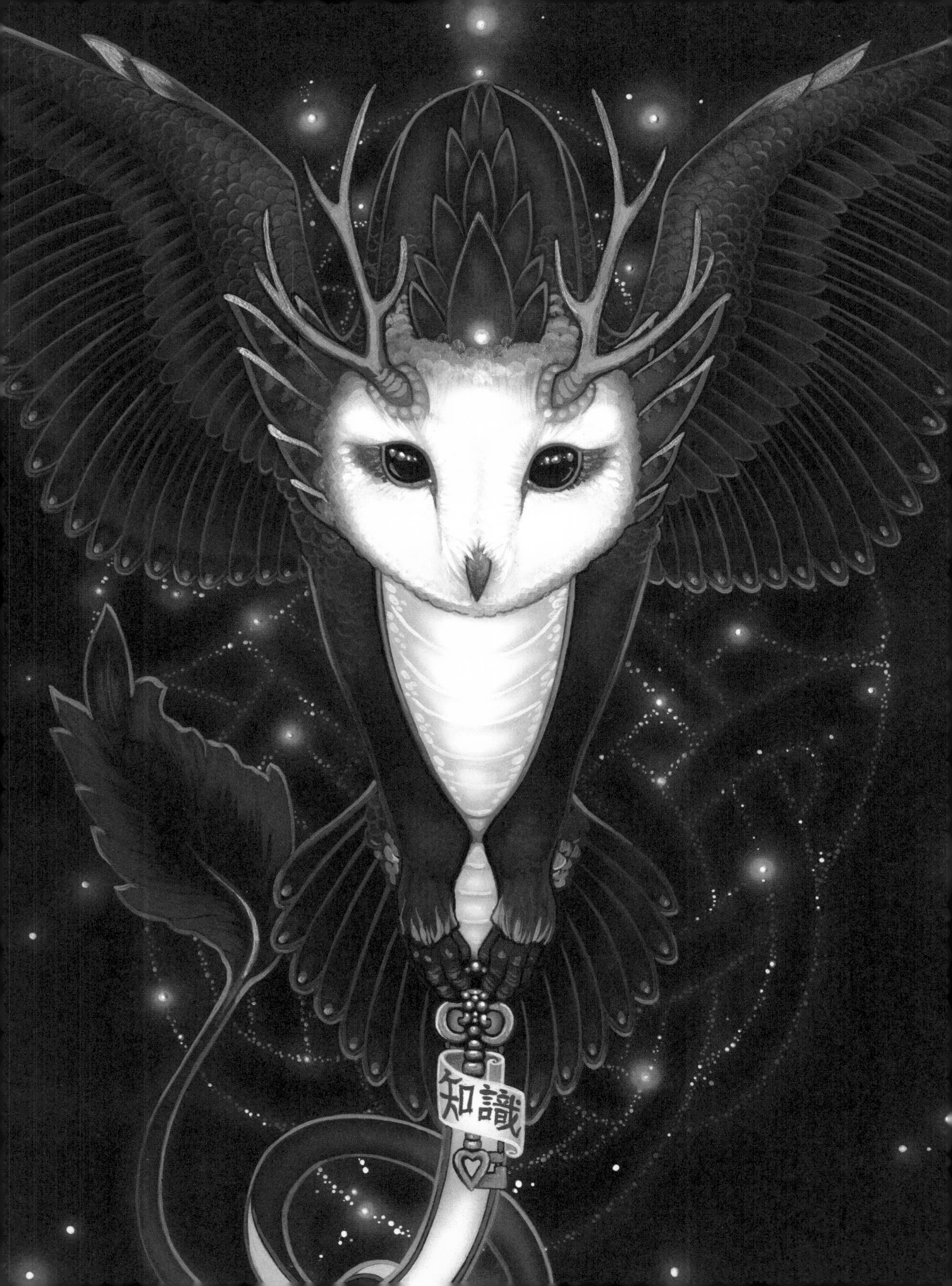
知識

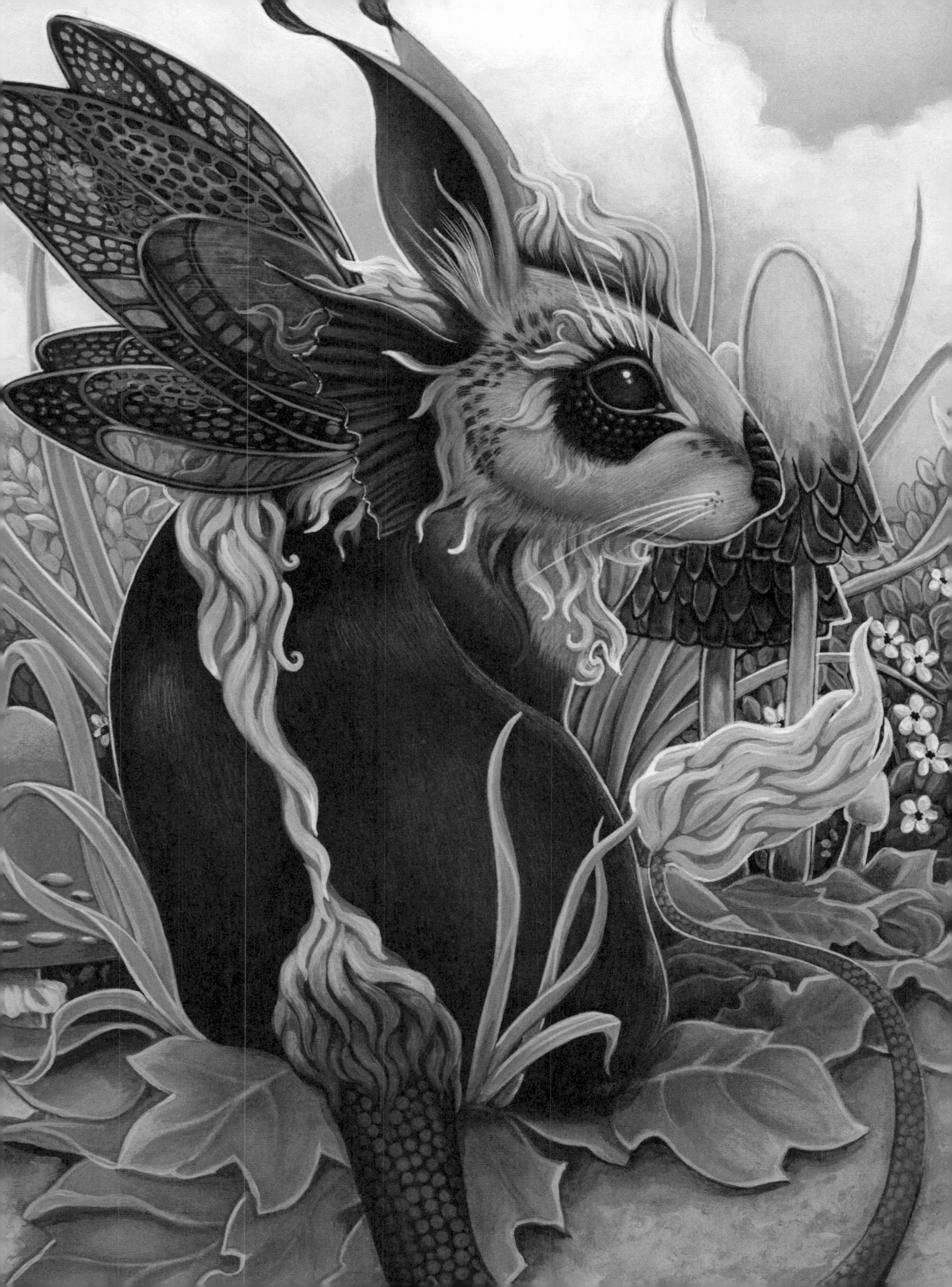

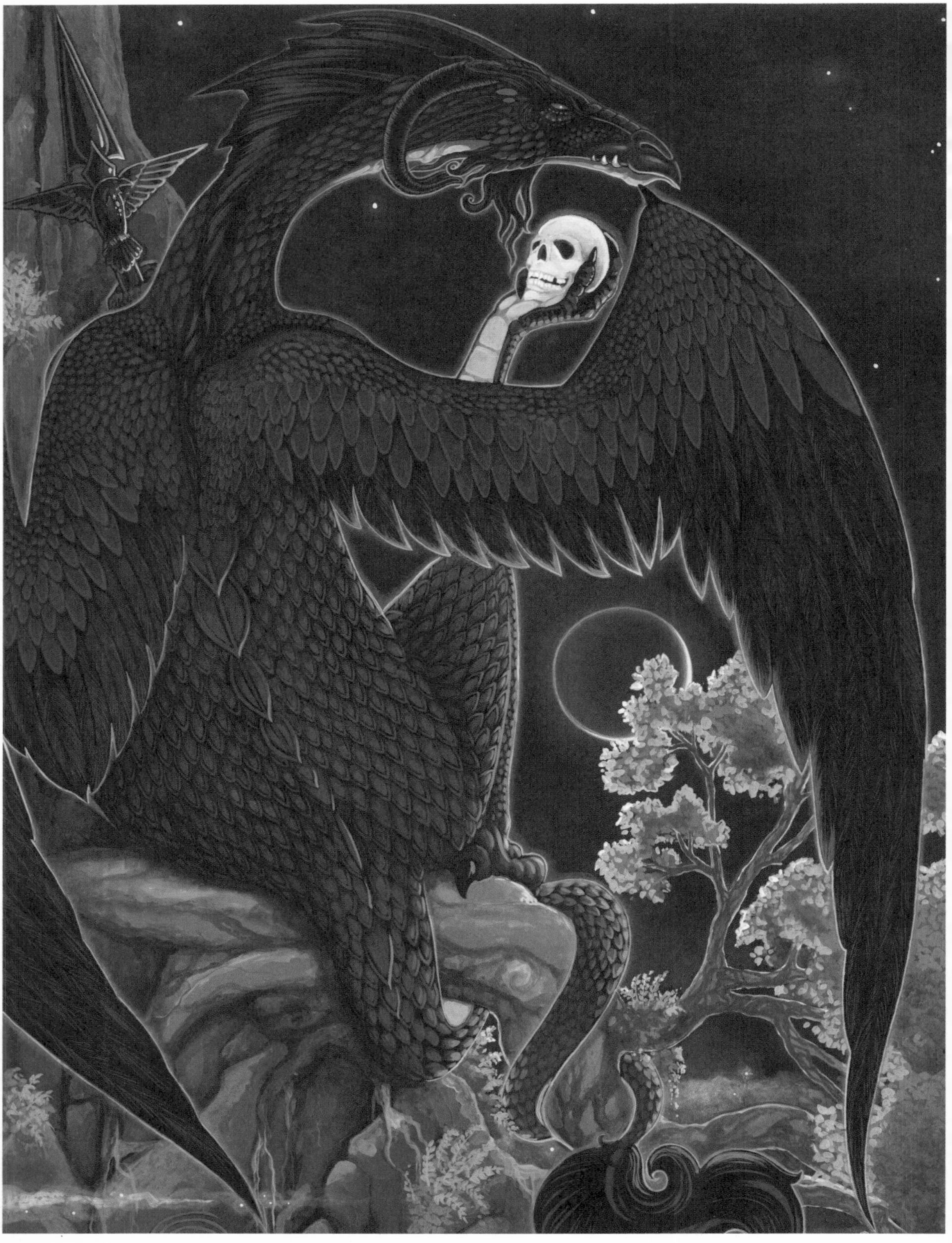

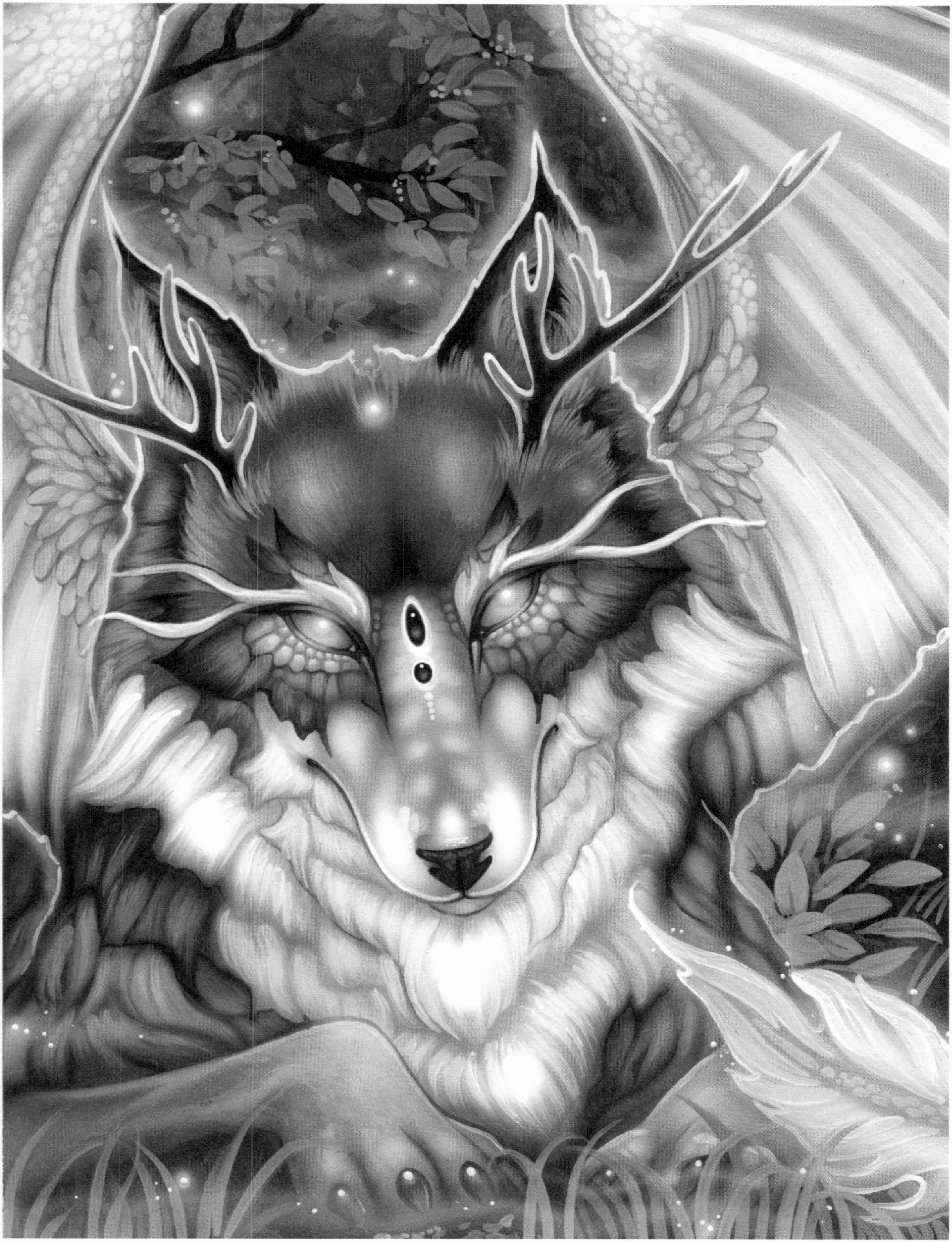

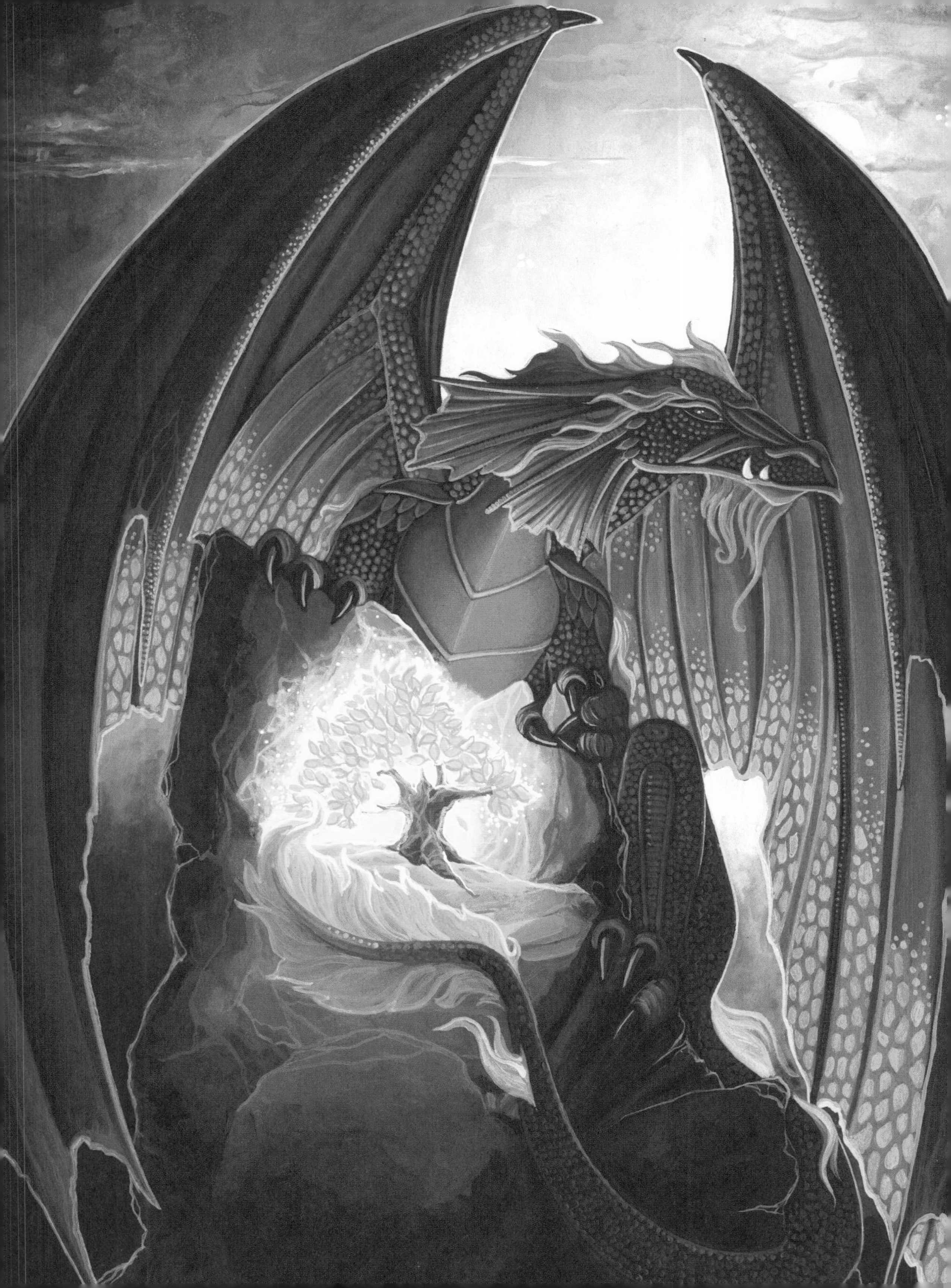

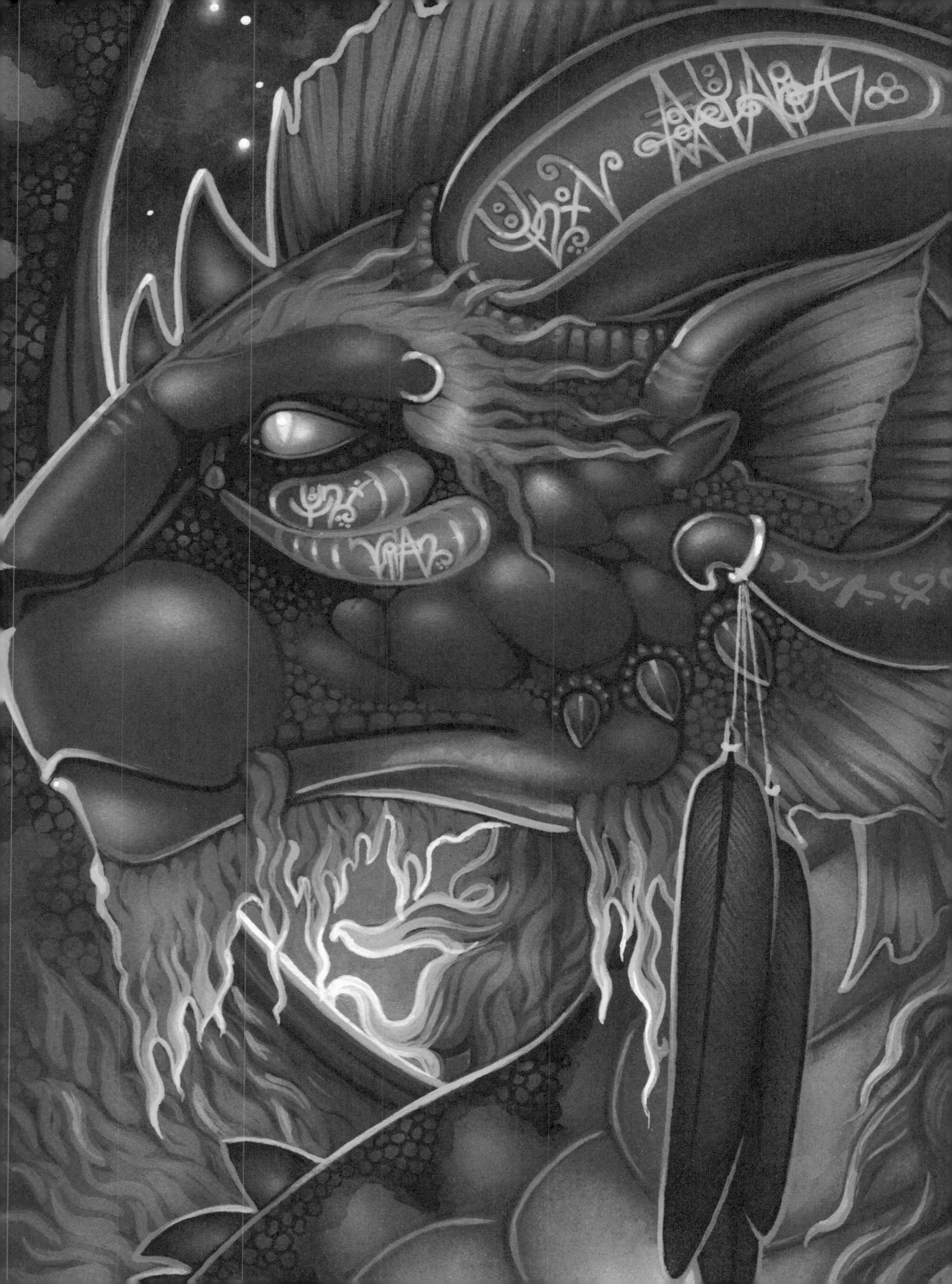

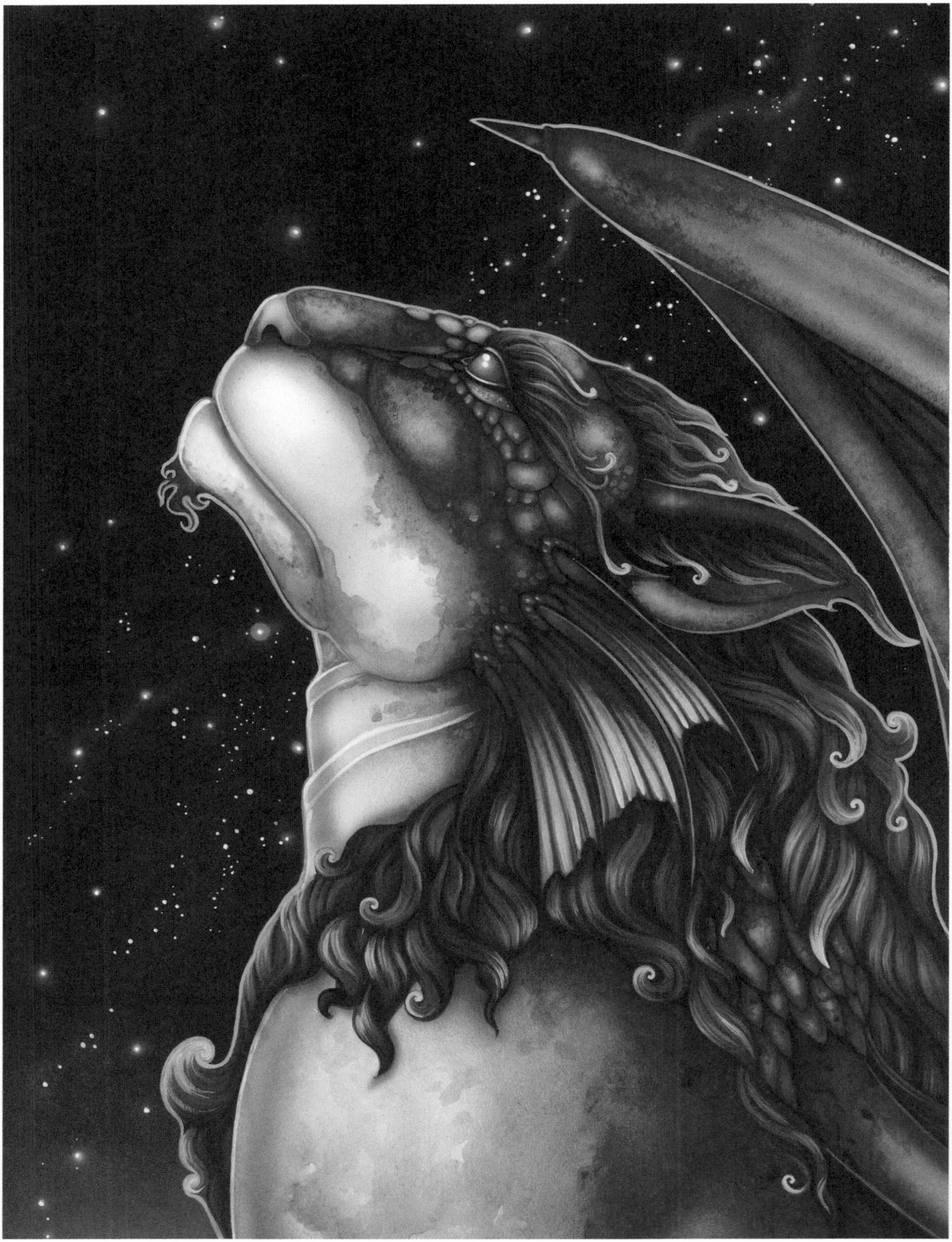

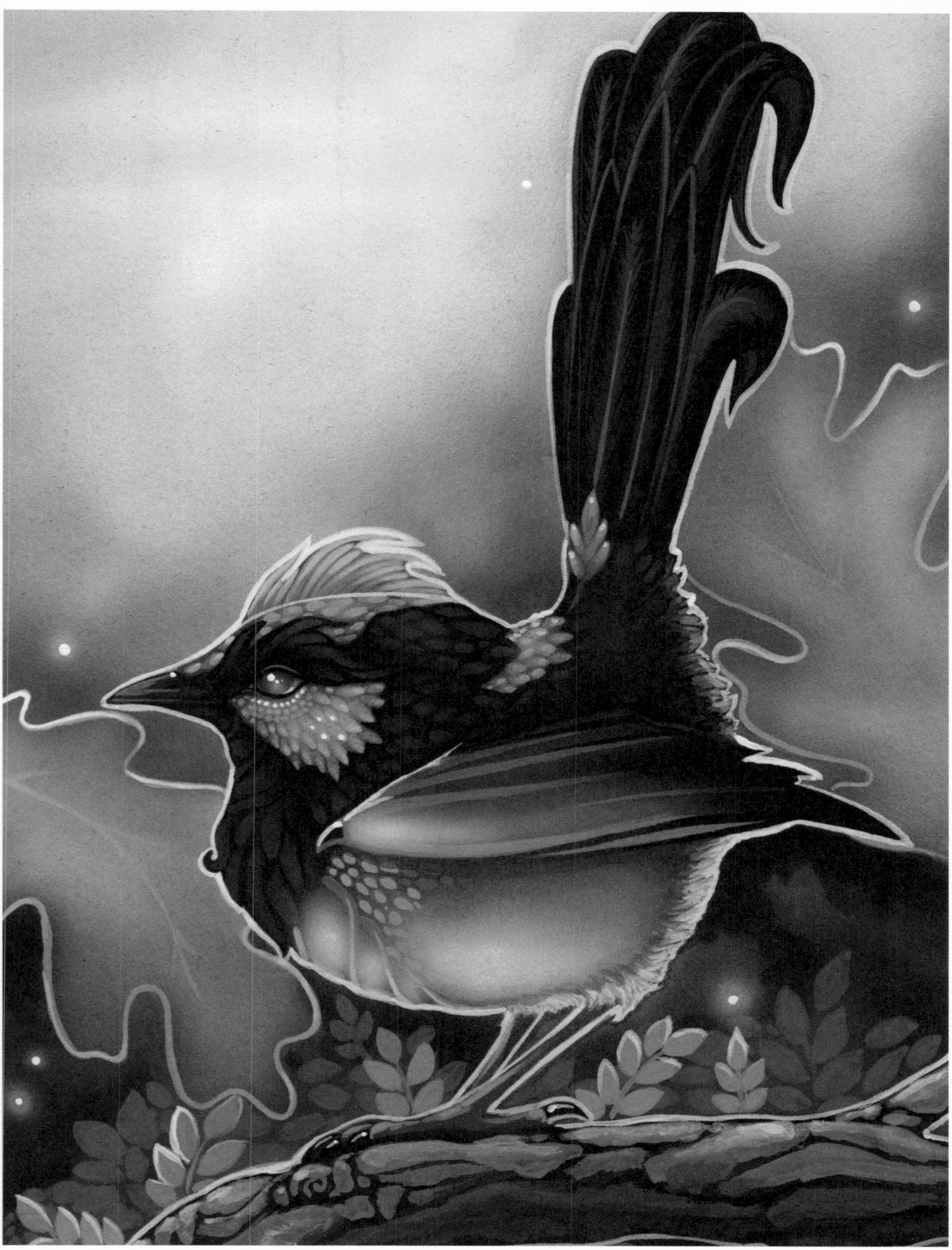

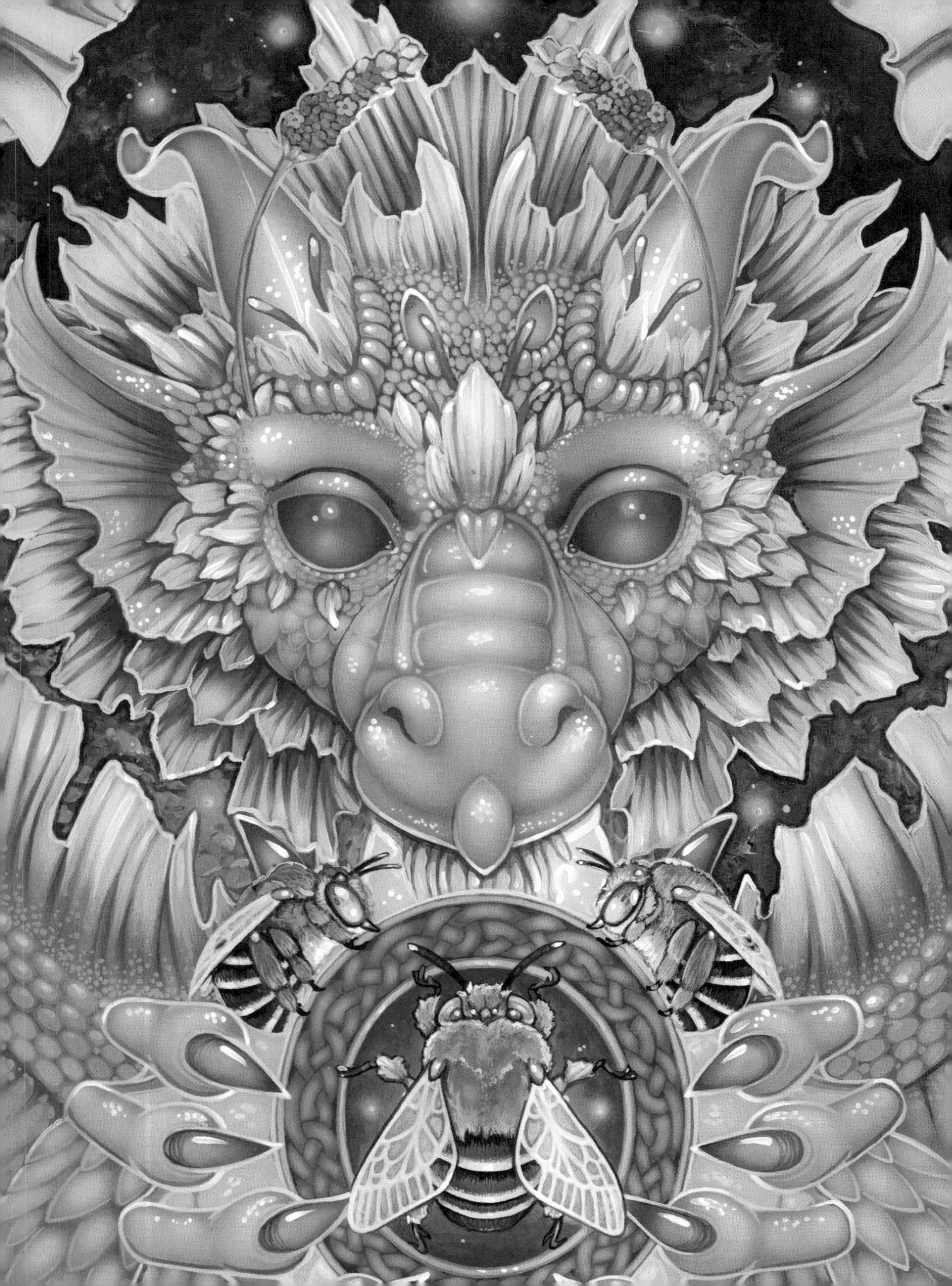

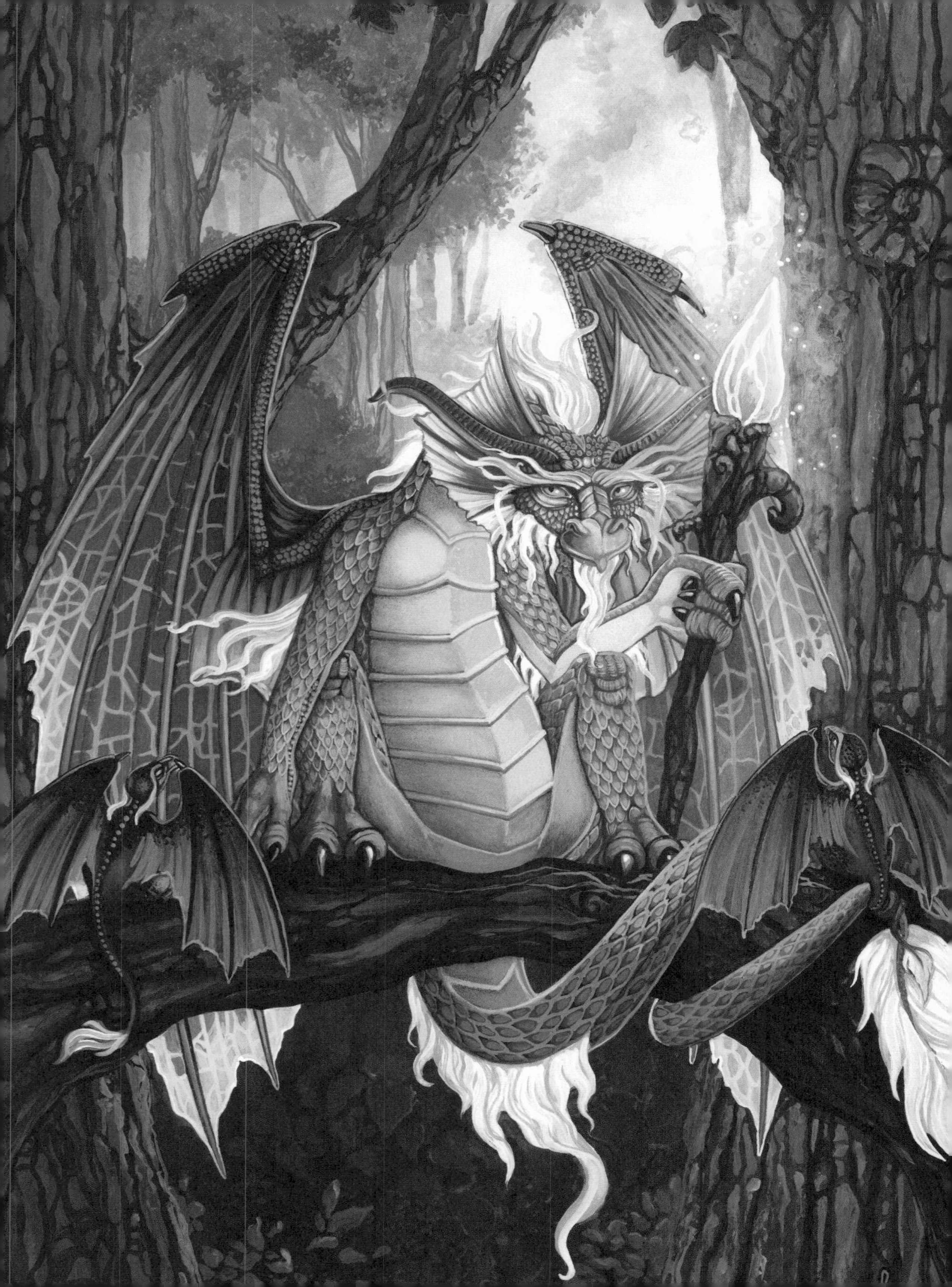

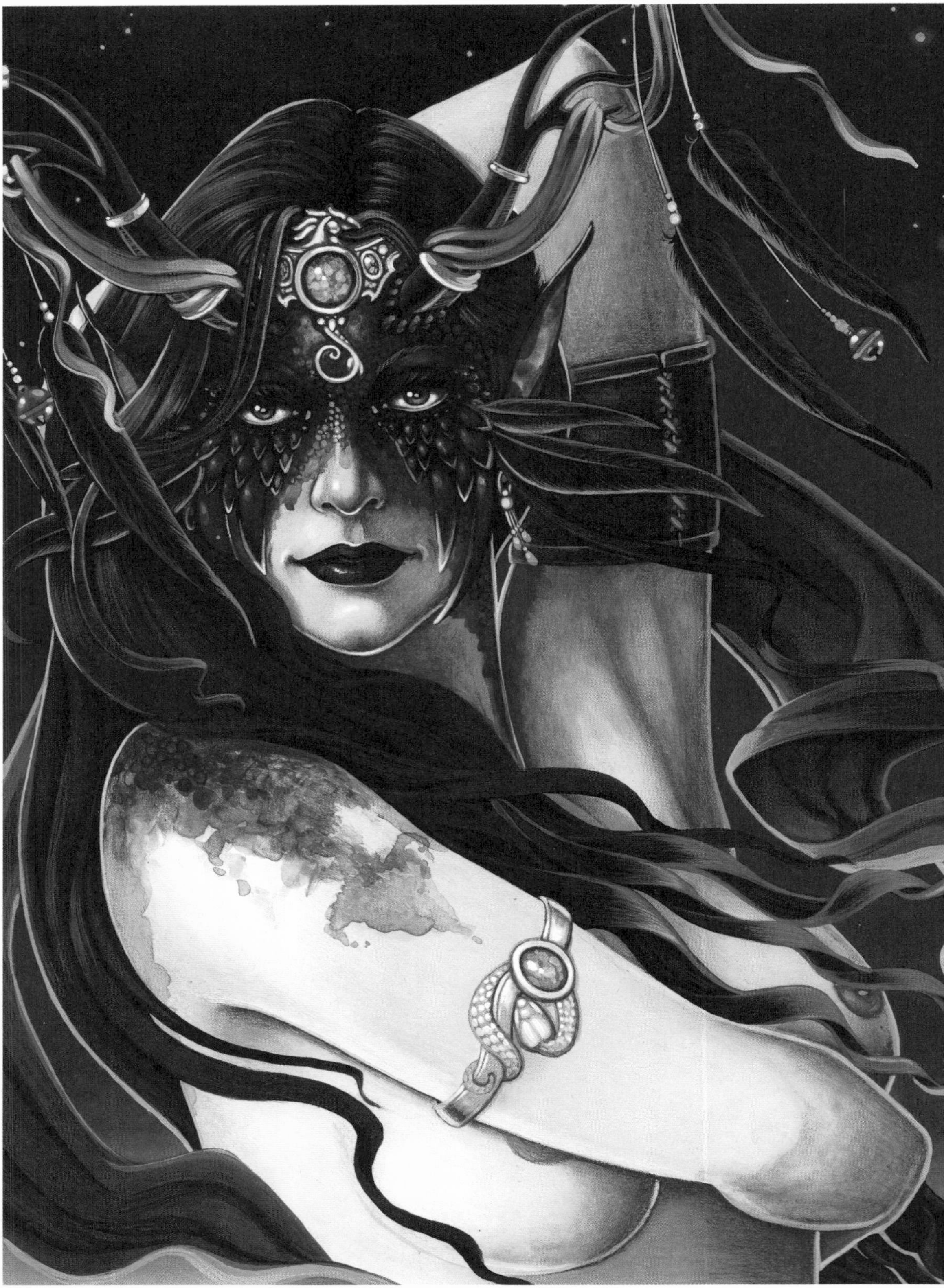

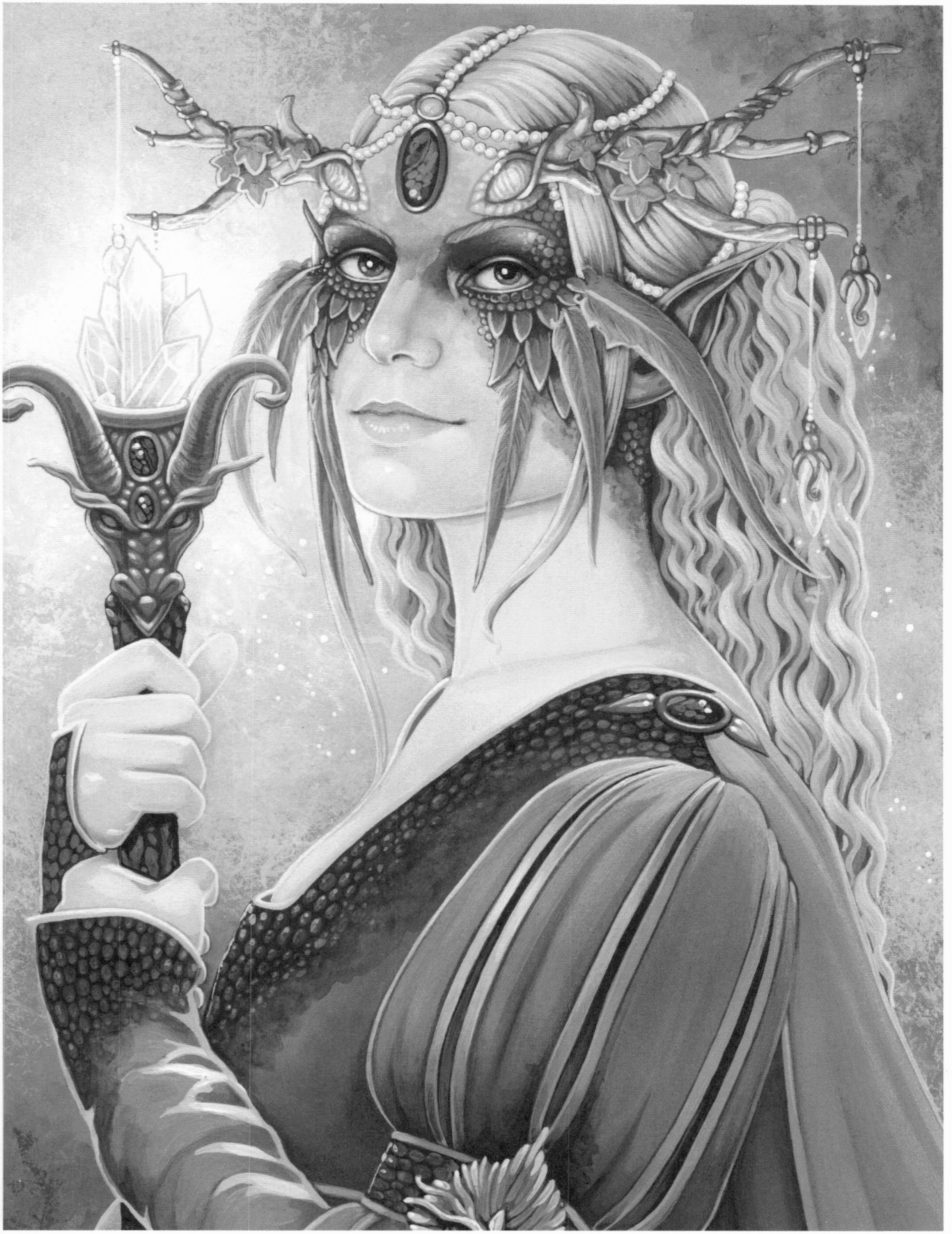

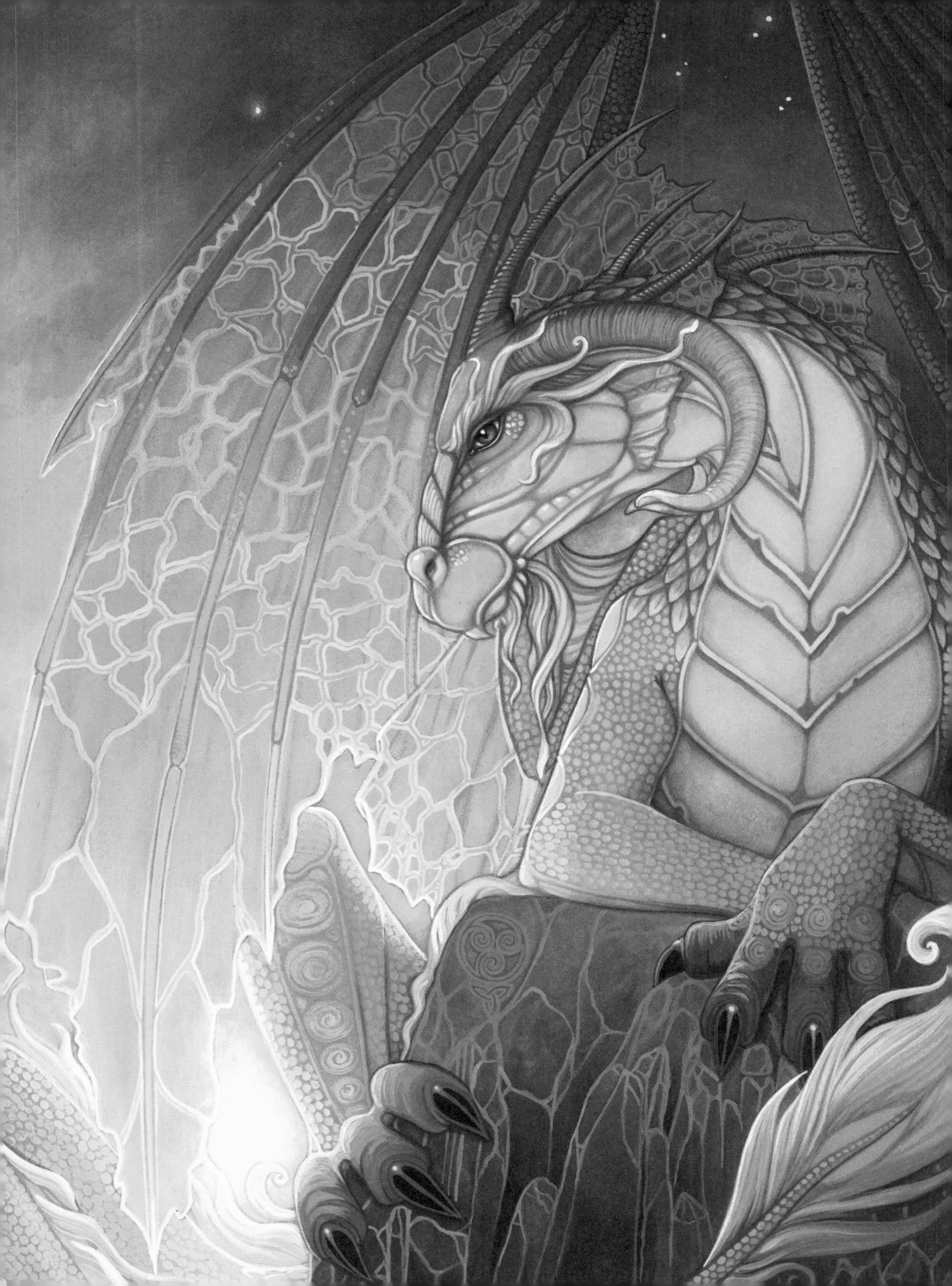

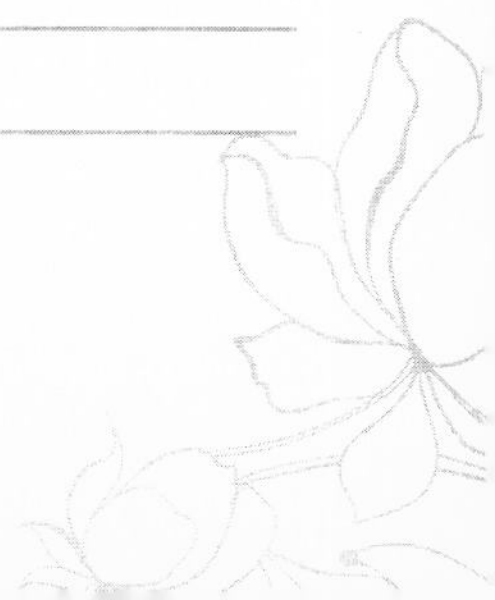

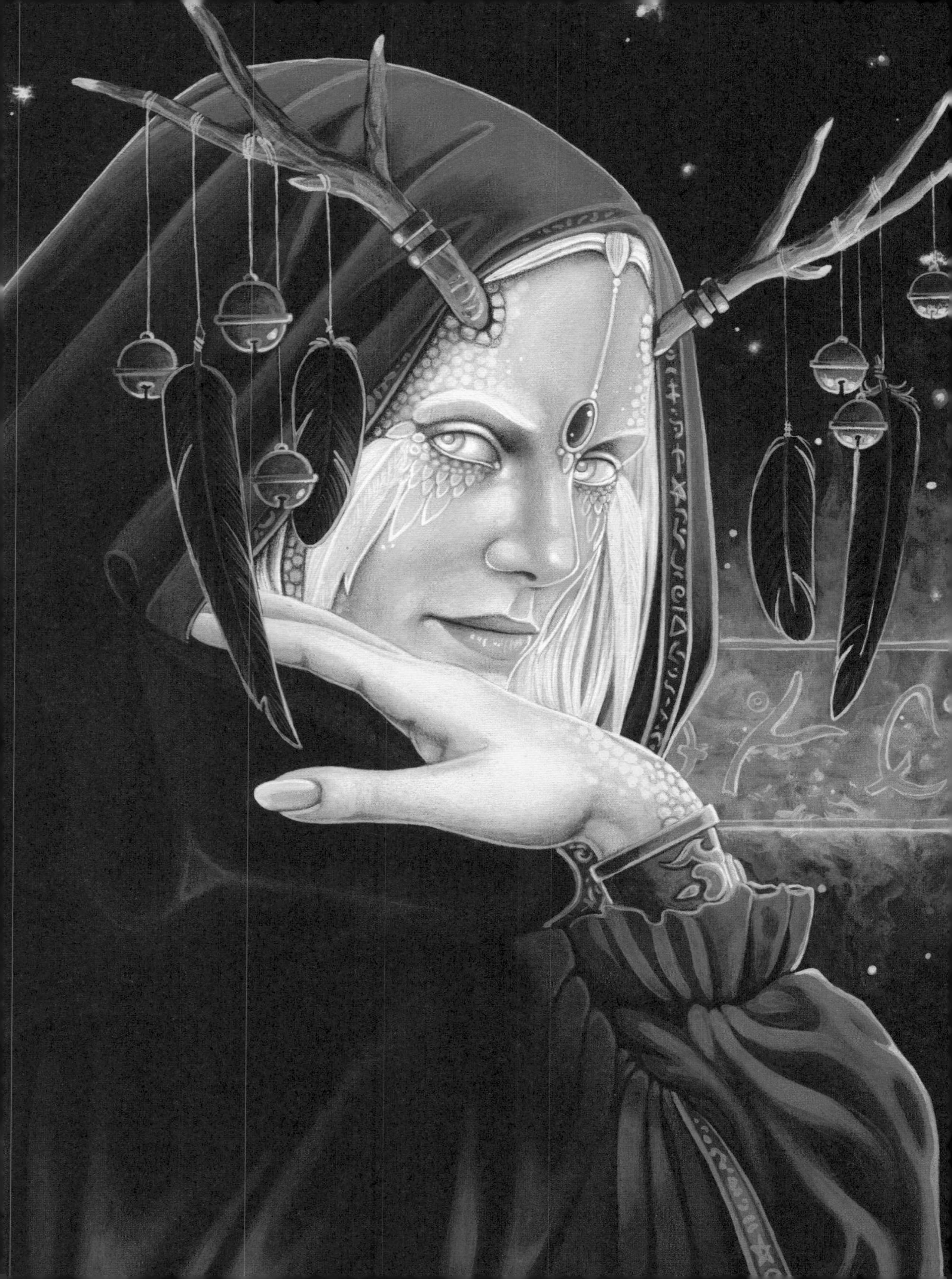

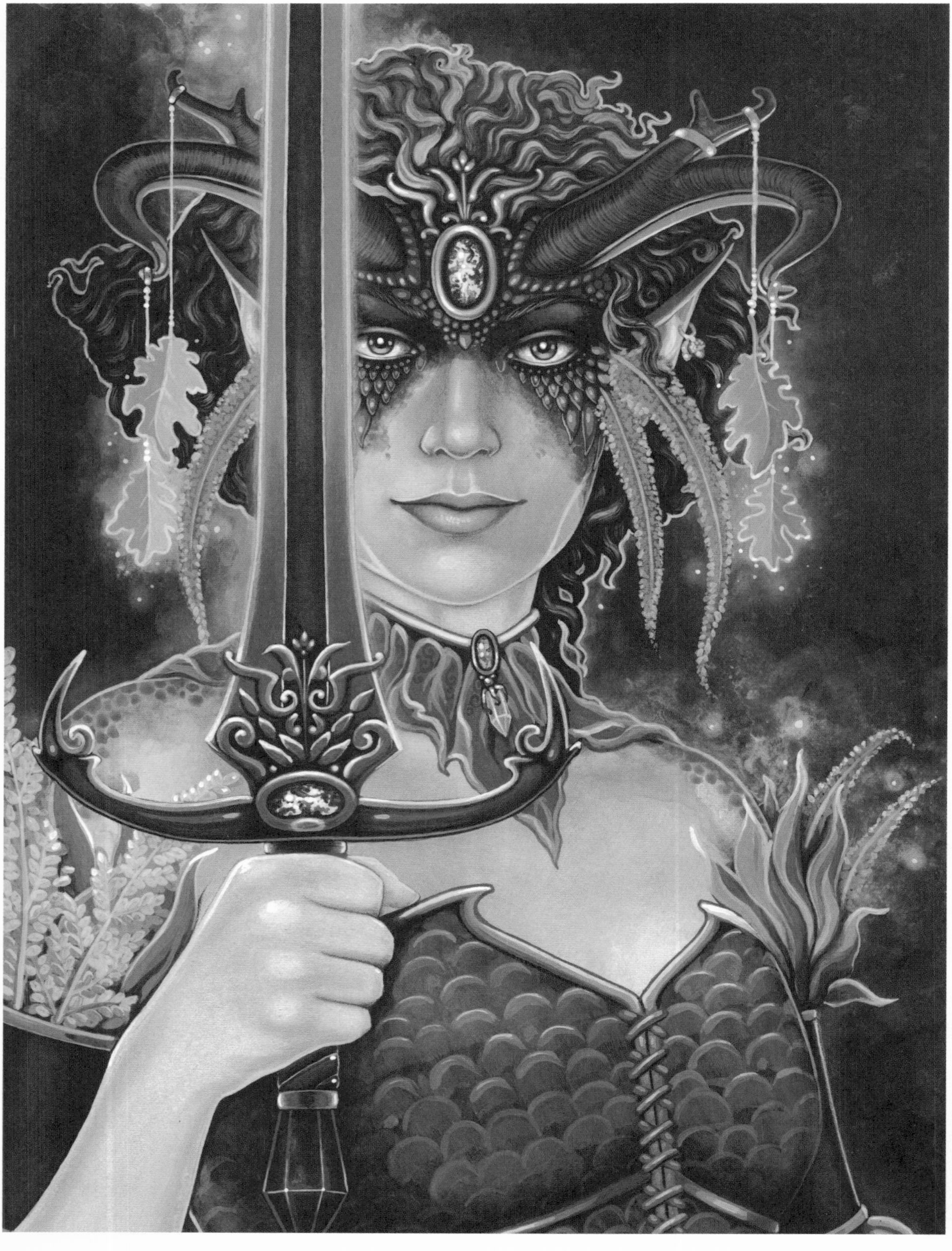

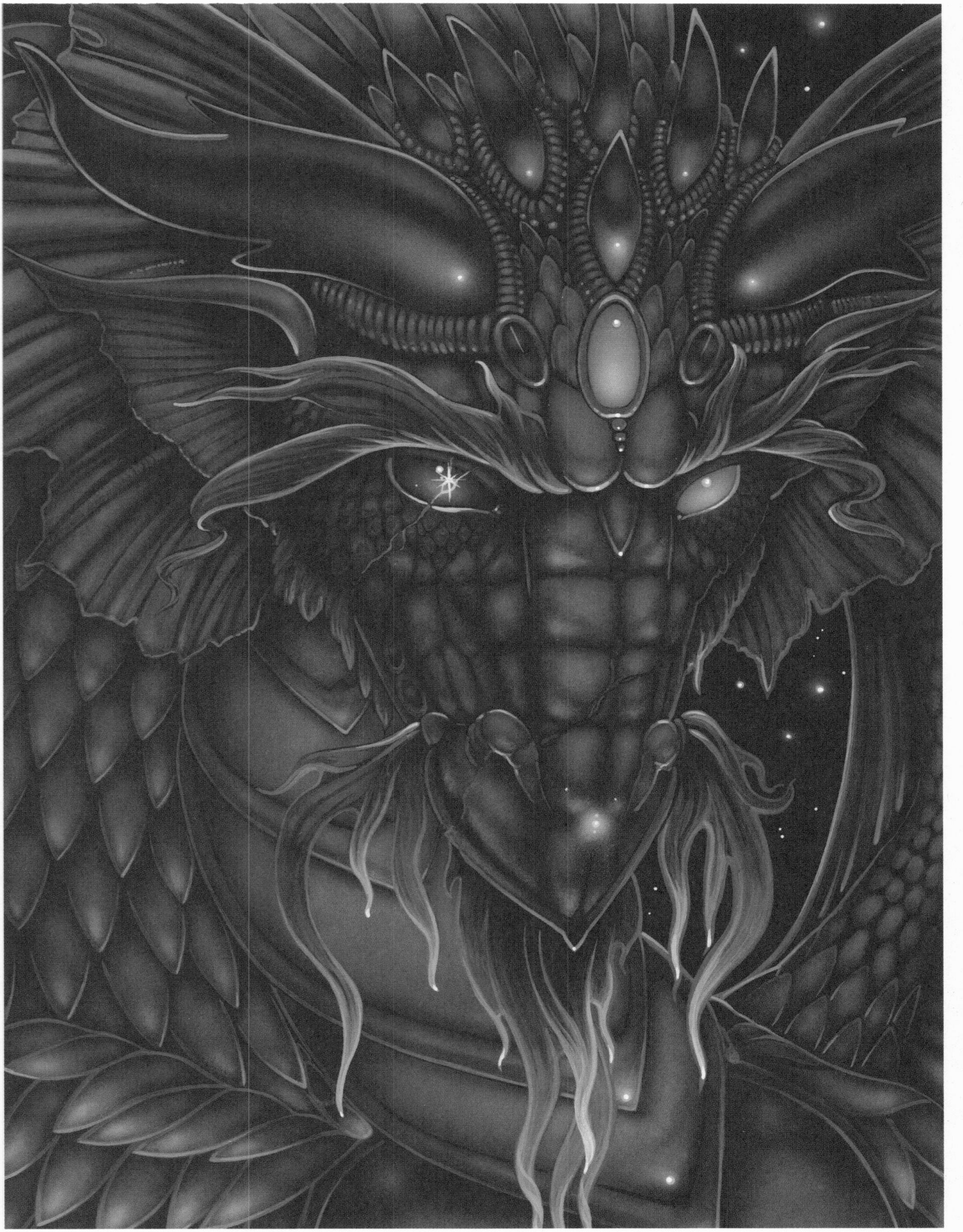

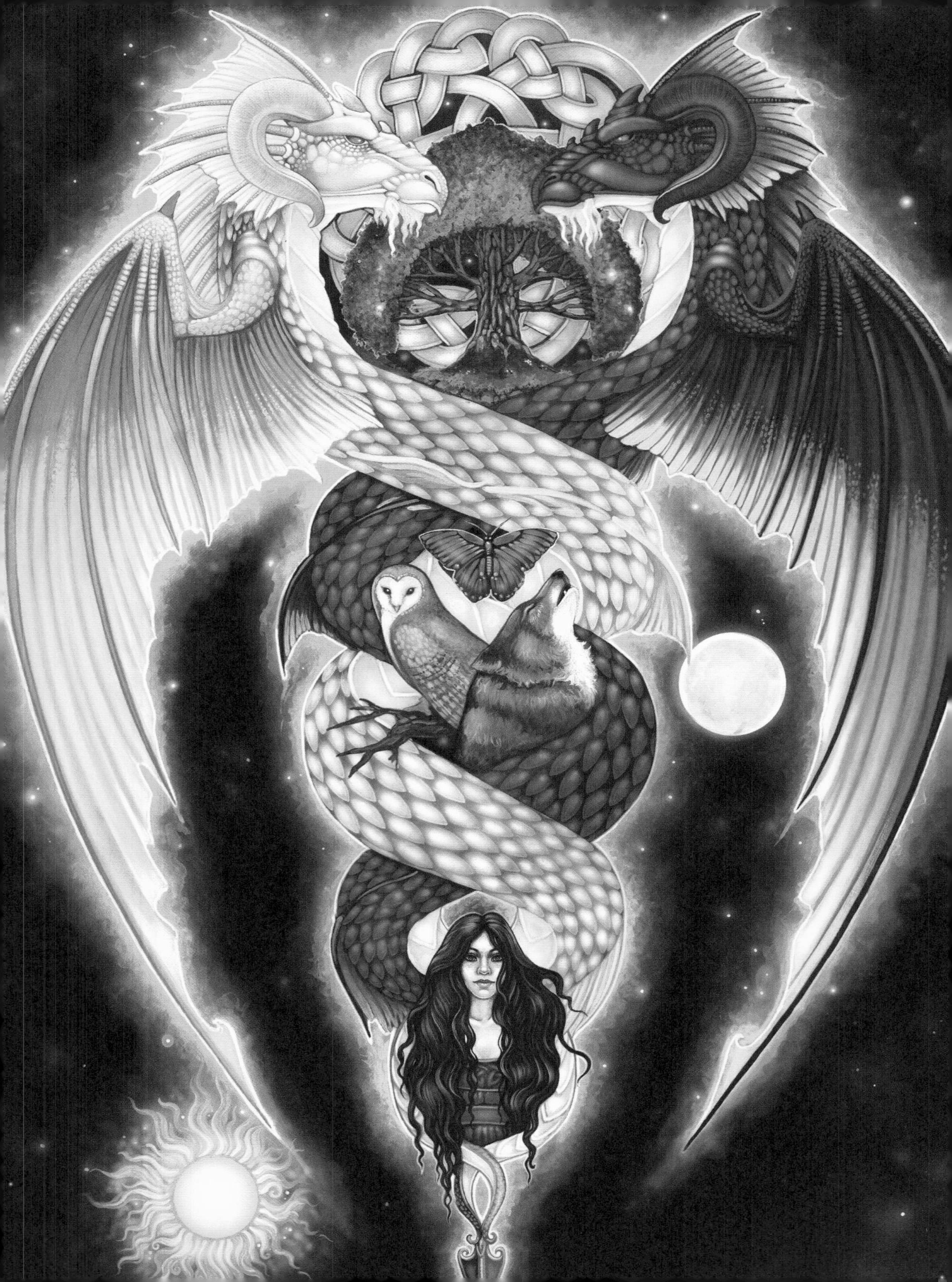

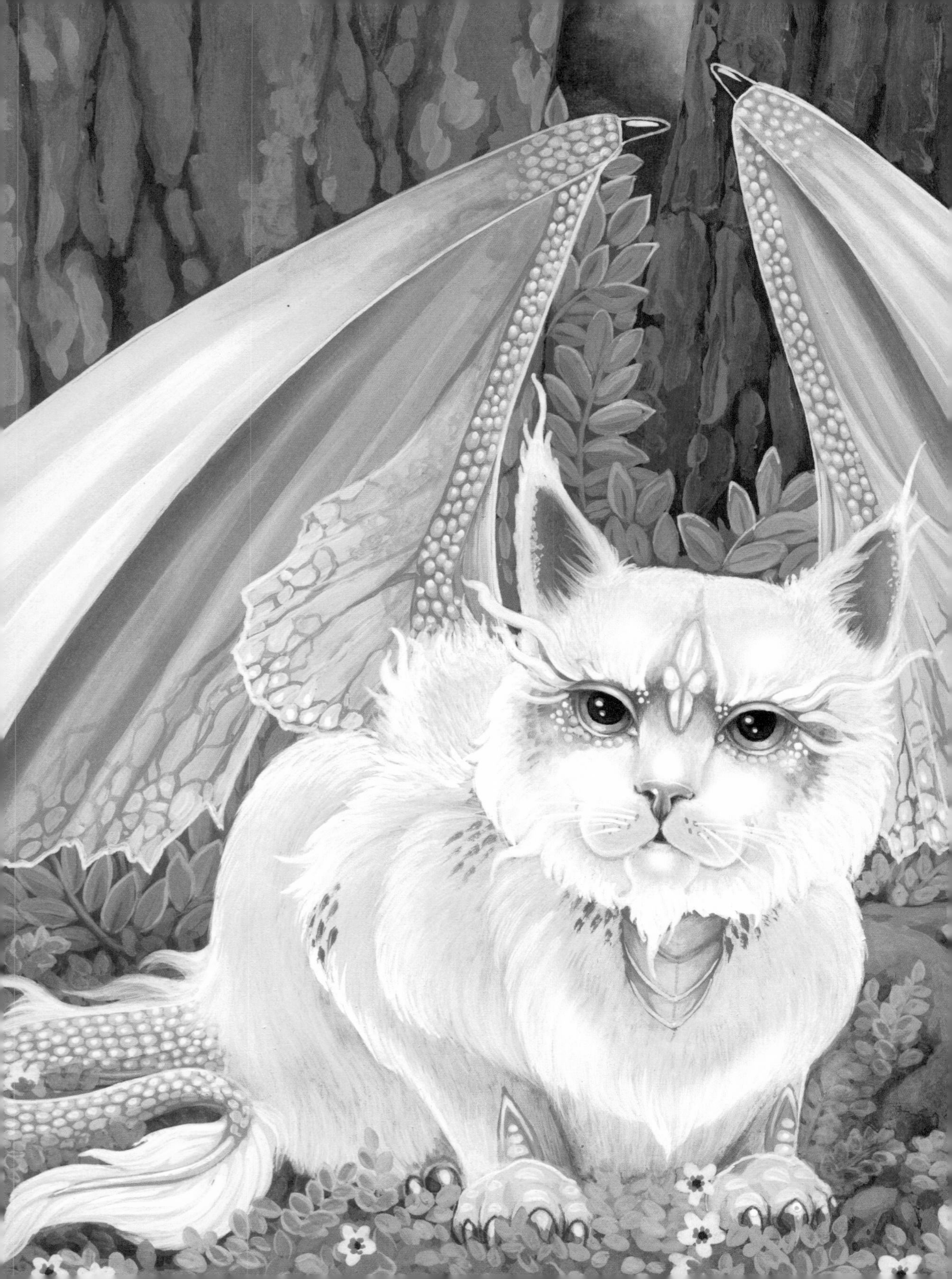

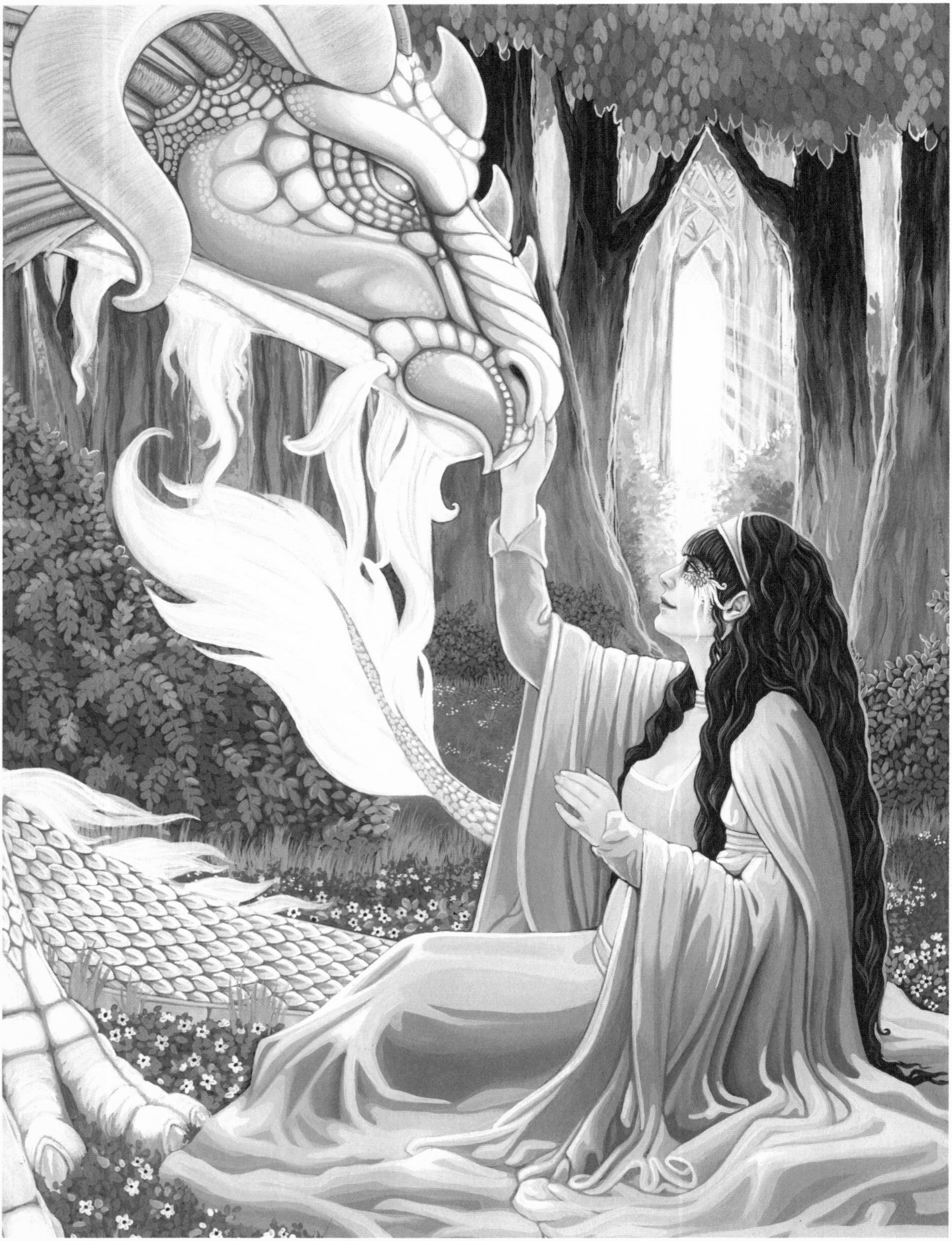

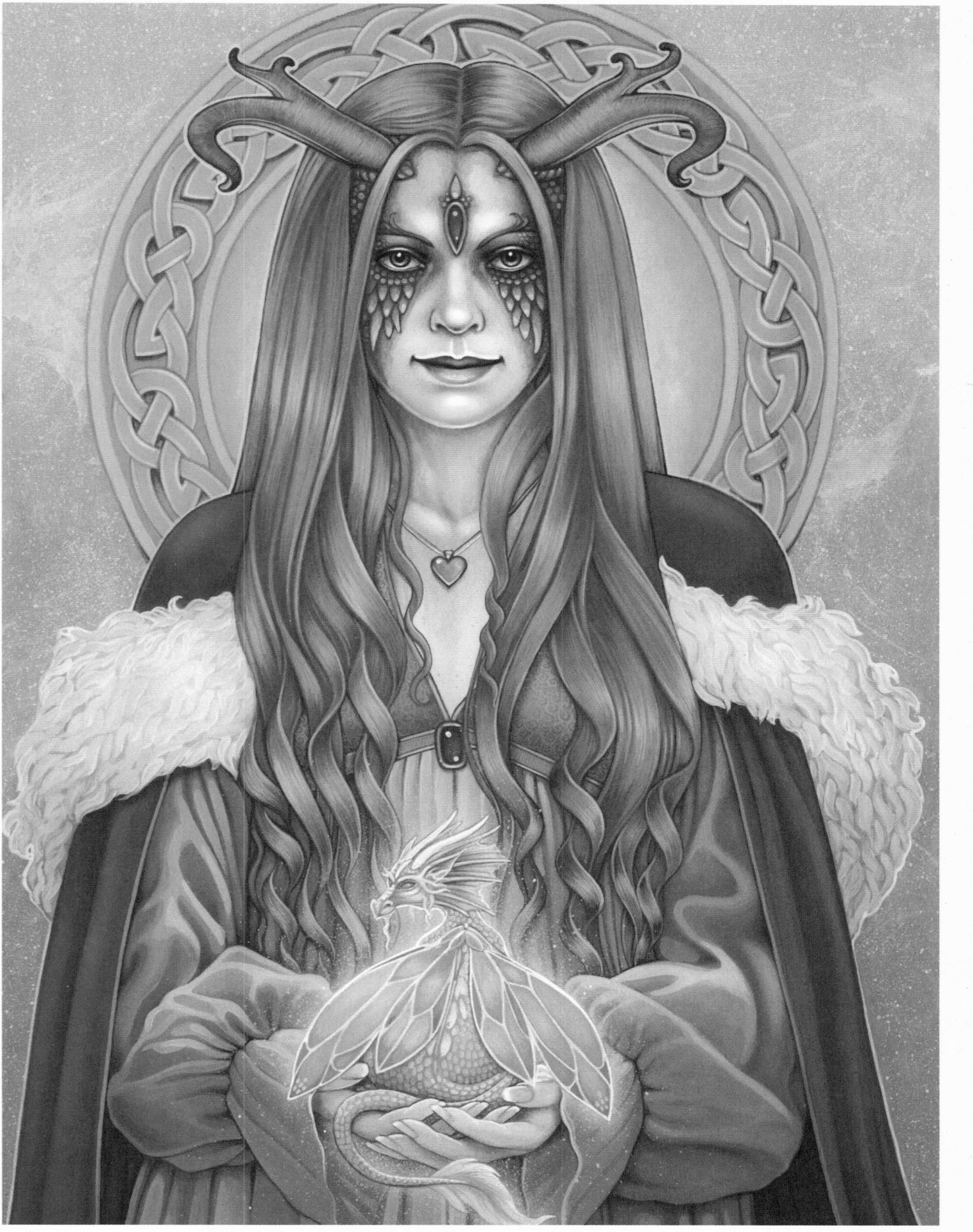

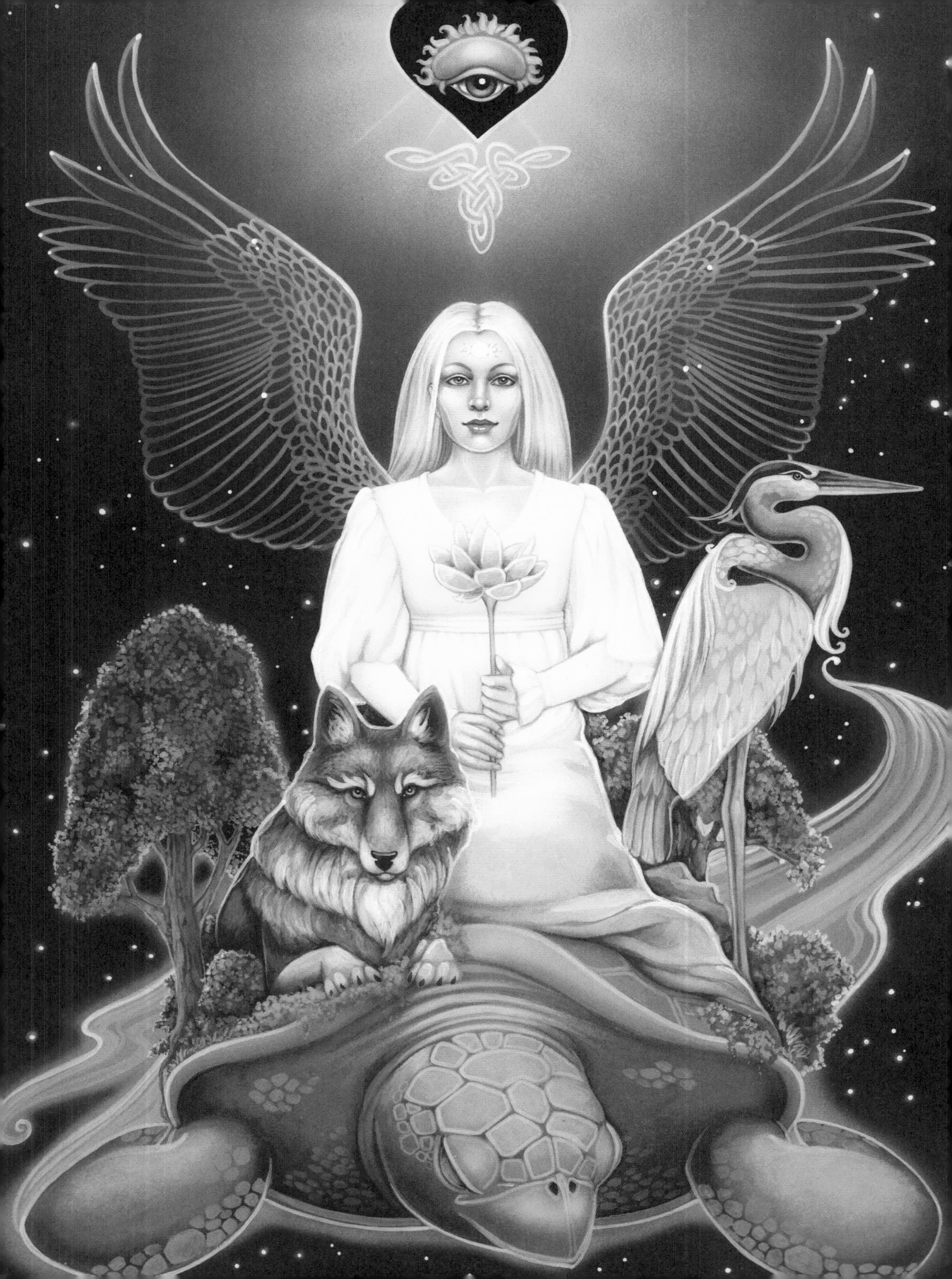

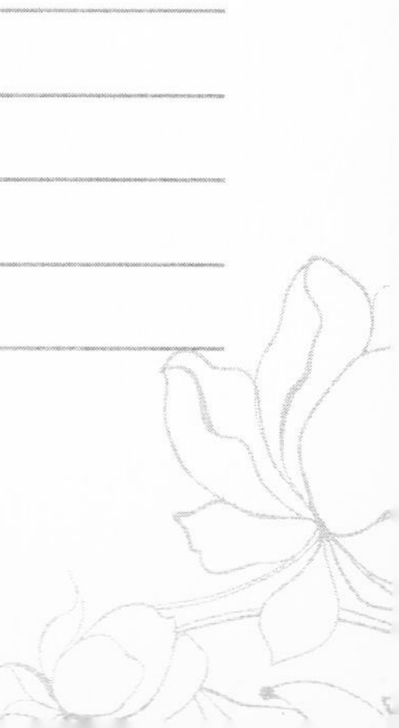

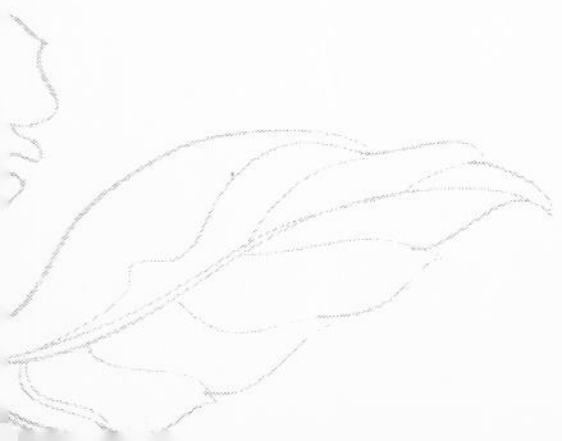

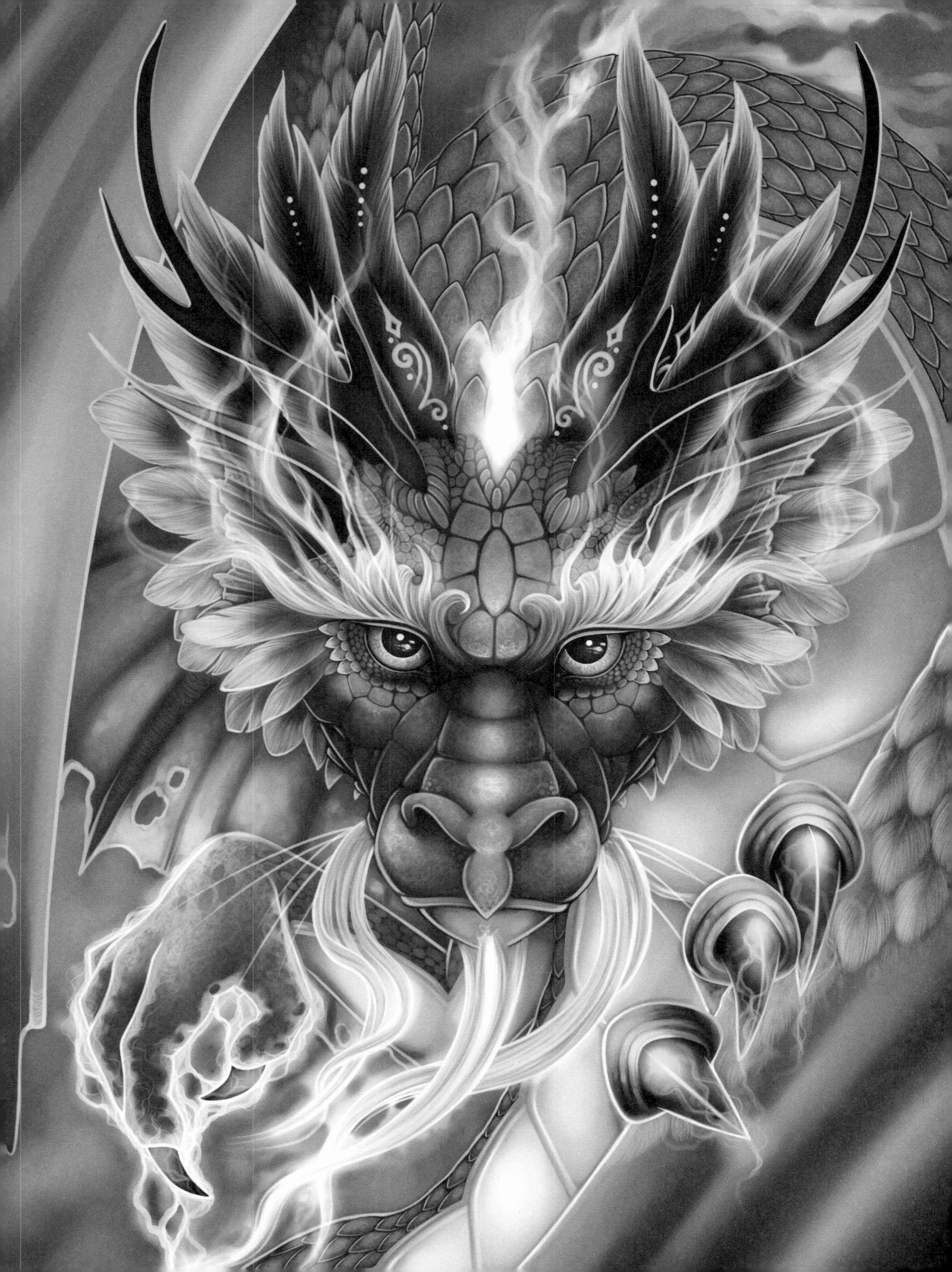

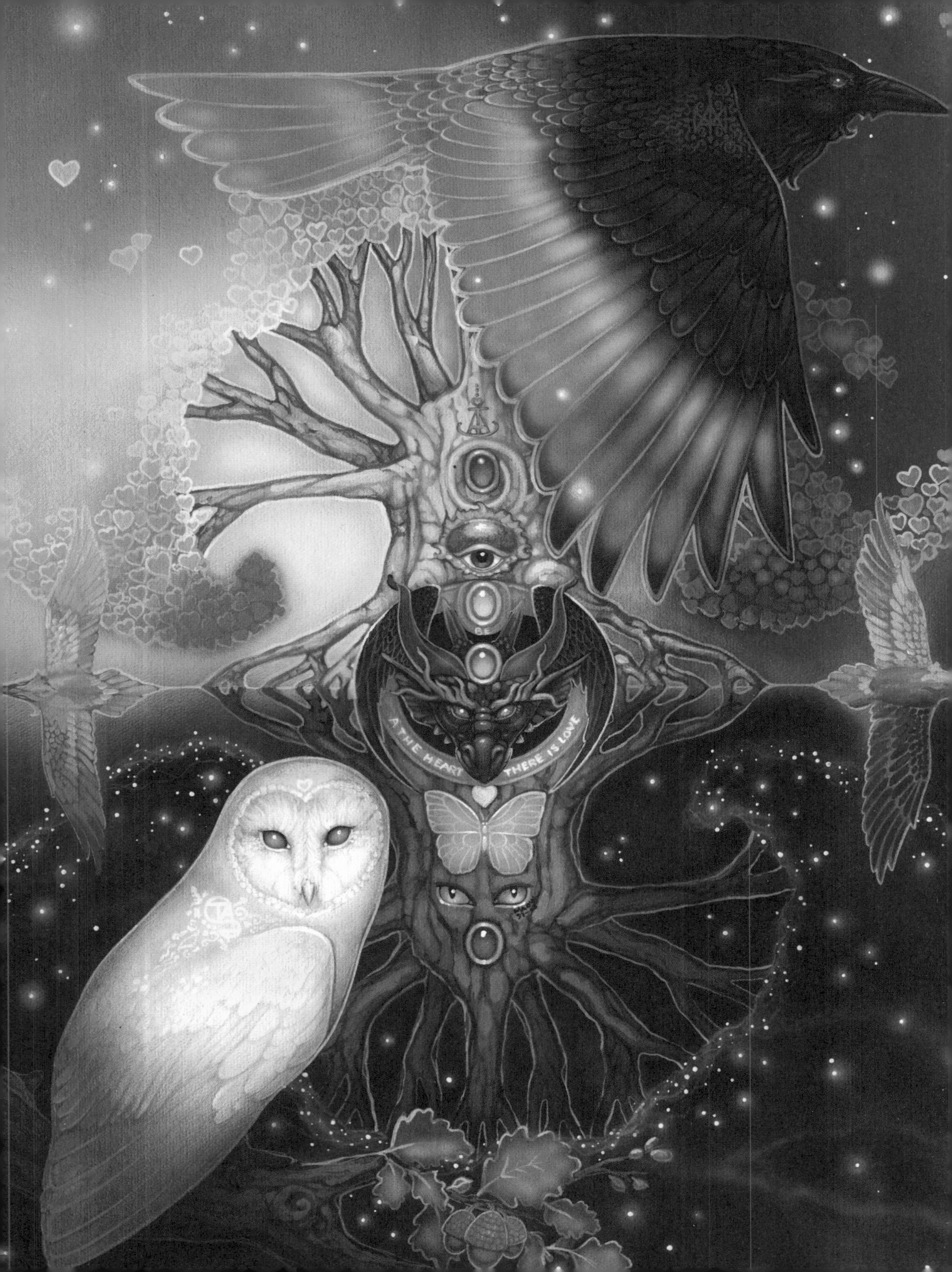
A THE HEART
THERE IS LOVE